ASK THE VET

Questions & Answers for Dog Owners

Gary D. Norsworthy
DVM, Dipl ABVP

Sharon K. Fooshee
MS, DVM, Dipl ABVP, Dipl ACVIM

With contributions by

R. Charles Povey
BVSc, PhD, FRCVS

Illustrations by Rebecca Brebner

A Lifelearn Publication

Lifelearn Inc., Guelph, Ontario, Canada

Project Editor: Anne Behnan
Cover Design: Leah Aurini

MacNabb House
University of Guelph
Guelph, Ontario, Canada
N1G 2W1

ISBN 1-896985-01-7

Disclosure and Caution: Every care has been taken to provide accurate information. However knowledge is not absolute. Medical opinions differ. Drugs are subject to change in dosage, format, etc. The reader is urged to use the information in this book as an adjunct to, and not a substitute for, professional veterinary advice, based on a full and proper examination and knowledge of the patient. To purchase additional copies of this book call 1•800•375•7994 or Fax us at 1•519•767•1101.

PREFACE

Ask the Vet: Questions and Answers for Dog Owners

This book is based on a series of client information sheets that we (G.D.N., S.K.F.) prepared for use in our clinics, and subsequently was developed on disc by Lifelearn as a basis for veterinarians to adapt to their clinic use.

The topics covered are those that are the most frequently encountered health issues in dogs. The majority of dogs lead very healthy lives, but when they are sick and a visit to a veterinarian is necessary, very little of the doctor's explanation of the illness may be fully understood or remembered. This book will greatly help.

Prevention is better than cure. Many topics covered, such as 'Recommendations for owners of puppies,' 'Dental disease,' etc., will provide information as to how and when you can work with your veterinarian to maintain wellness of your pet.

'Emergencies and First Aid' will provide guidance in recognizing true emergencies and dealing with those situations until veterinary help can be obtained.

Gary D. Norsworthy
DVM, Dipl ABVP

Sharon K. Fooshee
MS, DVM, Dipl ABVP, Dipl ACVIM

R. Charles Povey
BVSc, PhD, FRCVS

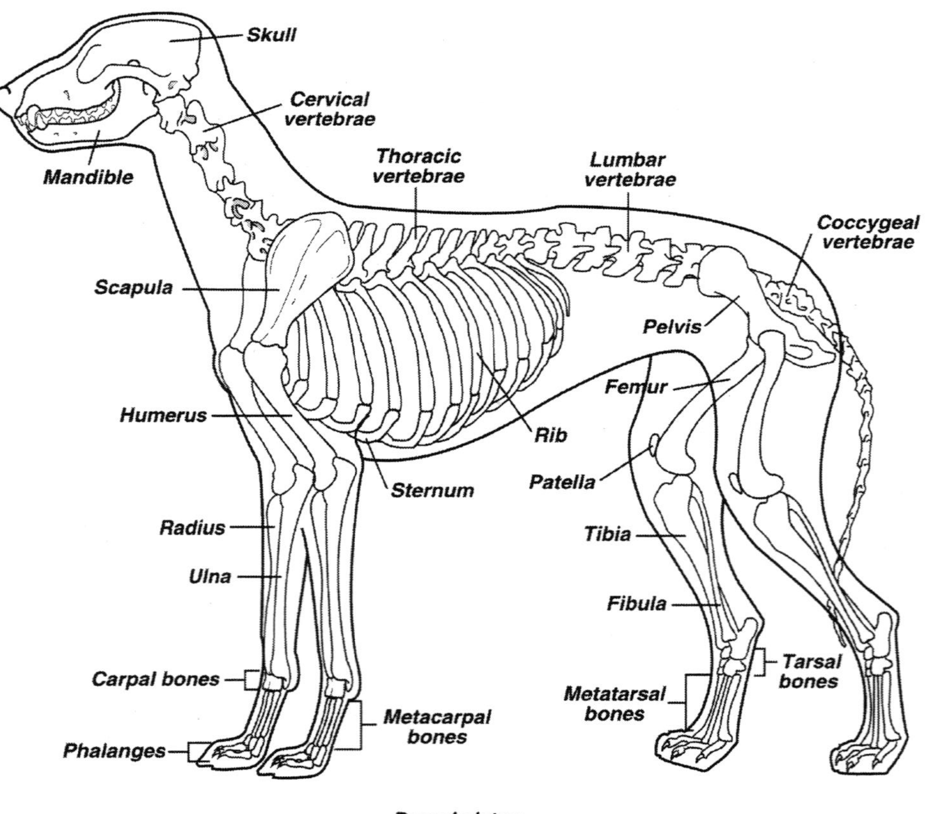

Dog skeleton

Table of Contents

AIRLINE TRAVEL WITH YOUR DOG

I'm planning to travel and would like to take my dog with me. What are some of the factors I need to consider before taking my dog on an airplane?

Having your dog along may add enjoyment to your trip. It is important to keep your dog's health and safety in mind when travelling, so be sure to check with the airline well in advance of your trip. Familiarize yourself with the airline's pet requirements so that you can avoid any last minute problems. Here are some basic tips for airline travel with your dog:

- Take direct flights and try to avoid connections and layovers. This eliminates missed baggage connections and the chance that your dog will be left in extreme weather.
- Many airlines will allow one pet in coach and one in first class, with some provisions. Some airlines limit the number of pets travelling within the cabin area so be sure to notify the airline that your dog will be travelling with you. Your dog must be in a standard cage that will fit under the seat and must not disturb your fellow travellers. Obviously, only small dogs qualify for this type of accommodation.
- Seek the advice of your veterinarian before travelling. Update all vaccinations. Take all necessary health papers with you. Determine whether a health certificate for the dog will be required at your point of destination. You might also inquire about possible requirements to quarantine your dog should you be travelling to a foreign country.
- If possible, use airlines that hand carry your dog (inside the cage) to and from the aircraft. Otherwise, the cage could simply be placed on a conveyor belt.
- Do not feed your dog for six hours before the flight; allow water until flight time. Water should be available in the cage. Give the dog fresh water as soon as it arrives at the destination.
- Avoid the busiest travel times so airline personnel will have extra time to handle your dog.
- Do not tranquilize your dog without first discussing it with your veterinarian.
- Make sure the cage has specific feeding and identification labels permanently attached.
- Baggage liability limitations apply to your dog. Check your ticket for liability limits or, better yet, speak directly with the airline. If you are sending an economically valuable pet, you may want to purchase additional liability insurance.
- Be aware that airline travel may pose a risk for dogs with a pre-existing medical problem. For example, you should give serious thought to travelling by plane with a dog who has kidney disease or heart disease. Also, one study has shown that short-faced breeds of dogs (English Bulldogs, Boston Terriers, Pekinese) do not travel well in certain situations. Discuss these issues with your veterinarian prior to travel.

What do I need to consider when buying a travel carrier or cage?

Your dog's travel cage will be its "home" for much of your trip. It's important to choose the right cage. Here are some helpful guidelines:

- The cage should be large enough for your dog to stand up and turn around freely.
- The walls of the carrier should be strong and waterproof. This will prevent crushing and waste (urine) leakage.
- There must be adequate ventilation on at least three sides of the cage.
- The cage must have sturdy handles for baggage personnel to use.
- The cage should have a water tray which is accessible from the outside so that water can be added if needed.
- Cover the bottom of the cage with an absorptive covering or underpad. Check with a pharmacy for the flat absorbent underpads designed for bedridden people with bladder control problems.

Pet stores, breeders, and kennels usually sell cages that meet these requirements. Some airlines also sell cages that they prefer to use. Check with the airline to see if they have other requirements.

Try to familiarize your dog with the travel cage before you leave for your trip. Let your dog play inside with the door both open and closed. This will help eliminate some of your dog's stress during the trip.

Is there any other advice which might be useful as I prepare for my trip?

By applying a few common sense rules, you can keep your travelling dog safe and sound.

- Arrange ahead of time to stay in a hotel that allows pets. Many bookstores carry travel guidebooks with this type of information.
- Make sure that your dog wears a collar with an identification tag securely fastened. It should have your name, address, and telephone number.
- Always travel with a leash-harness for your dog. This is more secure than a collar. Familiarize your dog with the harness before the trip. Attach your dog's leash while it is still inside the cage. Outside the cage, a frightened dog can easily run away before you have a chance to secure it.
- If you leave your dog unattended in lodging rooms, make sure that there is no opportunity for escape.
- Leave the dog in the cage or in the bathroom. Be sure to inform housekeeping personnel of your dog and ask that they wait until you return before entering the room. Use "Do Not Disturb" signs.
- Should your pet get lost, contact the local animal control officer.

Remember, advance planning is vital to make the trip an enjoyable experience for both you and your dog.

ANAL SAC DISEASE

What are anal sacs?

The anal sacs are located on either side of the anus at the 9:00 and 3:00 positions; they are positioned just under the skin. They connect to the anus by means of small canals or ducts. Anal sacs produce and store a dark, foul-smelling fluid. These are the same type of organs that a skunk has to scare away its enemies. Although dogs can use these for the same purpose, most dogs live in an environment that has no enemies. Because the sacs are rarely emptied, the fluid builds up, solidifies, and becomes an ideal environment in which bacteria can grow.

What disorders can occur in the anal sacs?

There are 3 diseases that occur in the anal sacs.

1) **Impaction**

   When the fluid becomes thick and solidified, the condition is called impaction.

2) **Infection**

   When bacteria grow in this material producing a yellow or bloody pus, the condition is called infection.

3) **Abscess**

   When the infection builds to create a hot, tender swelling in the sac, the condition is called an abscess. When the abscessed material overflows the sac, the skin over the sac breaks open, and the pus drains onto the skin.

How will I know if my dog is having problems with its anal sacs?

Symptoms of anal sac disease are:

- Scooting or dragging the anal area.
- Excessive licking under the tail.
- Pain, sometimes severe, near the tail or anus.
- A swollen area on either side of the anus.
- Bloody or sticky drainage on either side of the anus.

How are the various anal sac diseases treated?

The treatment for **impaction** is to express (squeeze out) the sacs and clean out the solidified material. For **infection**, the sacs must be expressed and antibiotics administered to kill the bacteria. If the sacs **abscess**, the abscess must be surgically drained and antibiotics administered.

My dog has had several bouts of anal sac disease. Is there a long-term cure?

Many dogs have recurrent anal sac disease. Some breeds of dogs, such as Poodles, commonly have problems. The anal sacs of obese dogs do not drain well, and thus these dogs are predisposed to recurrent problems. If a dog has several episodes of anal sac disease, the anal sacs can be removed surgically. Because these sacs are virtually unused, there is no loss to the dog. It is the only way to permanently cure the problem.

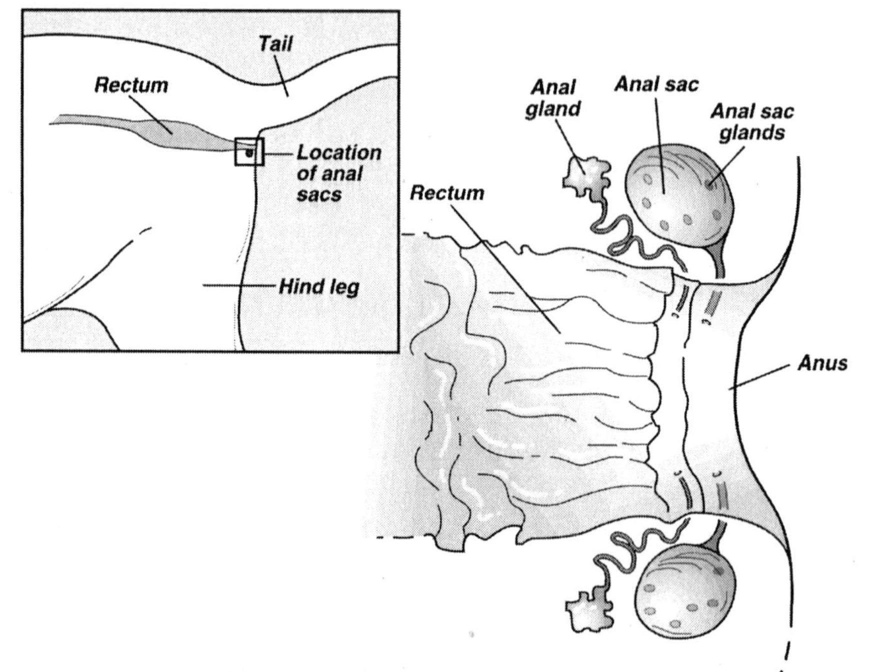

Diagram to show position of anal sacs.

Are there any complications of the surgery?

Surgery requires general anesthesia which always carries some degree of risk, whether the patient is a dog or a person. However, modern anesthetics make this risk very minimal for dogs that are otherwise healthy. Some dogs will experience lack of good bowel control. They may drop fecal balls as they walk. This occurs because the nerves that control the anus are very near the anal sacs and may be damaged during surgery. However, this is almost always a temporary problem that will resolve itself in a few days to a couple of weeks.

My dog frequently leaves a foul-smelling drop of liquid on the furniture. Is this related?

Some dogs are born with anal canals that do not close well. The ducts are constantly draining anal sac fluid and these dogs leave a foul-smelling drop where they have been. There does not appear to be any way to stop this, and these dogs do not outgrow this problem. This is another reason for anal sac removal.

What are bladder stones?

Bladder stones, more correctly called uroliths, are rock-like collections of minerals that form in the urinary bladder. They may occur as a large, single stone or as dozens of stones the size of large grains of sand or pea gravel.

Are these the same as gall stones or kidney stones?

No. Gall stones are in the gall bladder, and kidney stones are in the kidney. Although the kidneys and urinary bladder are both part of the urinary system, kidney stones are usually unrelated to bladder stones.

What problems do bladder stones cause?

The two most common signs of bladder stones are hematuria (blood in the urine) and dysuria (straining to urinate). Hematuria occurs because the stones mechanically irritate the bladder wall, causing bleeding from its surface. Dysuria occurs when stones obstruct the passage of urine out of the bladder. Large stones may cause a partial obstruction at the point where the urine leaves the bladder and enters the urethra; small stones may flow with the urine into the urethra and cause an obstruction there. When an obstruction occurs, urine cannot pass out of the body and the abdomen becomes very painful. Your dog may cry in pain, especially if pressure is applied to the abdominal wall. Hematuria and dysuria are the most common signs seen in dogs with bladder stones but with obstruction there is usually pain as well. We know this because when bladder stones are removed surgically, many owners tell us how much better and more active their dog feels.

Why do they form?

There are several theories of bladder stone formation. Each is feasible in some circumstances, but there is probably an interaction of more than one of them in each dog. The most commonly accepted theory is called the Precipitation-Crystallization Theory. This theory states that one or more stone-forming crystalline compounds is present in elevated levels in the urine. This may be due to abnormalities in *diet* or due to some previous disease in the bladder, especially *infection* with bacteria. When the amount of this compound reaches a threshold level, the urine is said to be supersaturated. This means that the level of the compound is so great that it cannot all be dissolved in the urine, so it precipitates and forms tiny crystals. These crystals stick together, usually due to mucus-like material within the bladder, and stones gradually form. As time passes, the stones enlarge and increase in number.

How fast do they grow?

Growth will depend on the quantity of crystalline material present and the degree of infection present. Although it may take months for a large stone to grow, some sizable stones have been documented to form in as little as two weeks.

How are they diagnosed?

Most dogs that have bladder infections do not have bladder stones. These dogs will often have blood in the urine and will strain to urinate, the same symptoms as a dog with bladder stones. Therefore, we do not suspect bladder stones just based on these clinical signs. Some bladder stones can be palpated (felt with the fingers) through the abdominal wall. However, failure to palpate them does not rule them out. Most bladder stones are visible on radiographs (x-rays) or an ultrasound examination. These procedures are performed if stones are suspected. This includes dogs that show unusual pain when the bladder is palpated, dogs that have recurrent hematuria and dysuria, or dogs that have recurrent bacterial infections in the bladder. Some bladder stones are not visible on radiographs. They are said to be radiolucent. This means that their mineral composition is such that they do not reflect the x-ray beam. These stones may be found with an ultrasound examination (if available) or with special radiographs that are made after placing a special dye (contrast material) in the bladder.

How are bladder stones treated?

There are two options for treatment. The fastest way is to remove them surgically. This requires major surgery in which the abdomen and bladder are opened. Following two to four days of recovery, the dog is relieved of pain and dysuria. The hematuria will often persist for a few more days, then it stops. Surgery is not the best option for all patients; however, those with urethral obstruction and those with bacterial infections associated with the stones should be operated on unless there are other health conditions that prohibit surgery.

The second option is to dissolve the stone with a special diet. This avoids surgery and can be a very good choice for some dogs. However, it has three disadvantages.

- It is not successful for all types of stones. Unless some sand-sized stones can be collected from the urine and analyzed, it is not possible to know if the stone is of the composition that is likely to be dissolved.
- It is slow. It may take several weeks or a few months to dissolve a large stone so the dog may continue to have hematuria and dysuria during that time.
- Not all dogs will eat the special diet. The diet is not as tasty as the foods that many dogs are fed. If it is not consumed exclusively, it will not work.

Can bladder stones be prevented?

The answer is a qualified "yes." There are at least four types of bladder stones, based on their chemical composition. If stones are removed surgically or if some small ones pass in the urine, they should be analyzed for their chemical composition. This will permit us to determine if a special diet will be helpful in preventing recurrence. If a bacterial infection causes stone formation, it is recommended that periodic urinalyses and urine cultures be performed to determine when antibiotics should be given.

BLASTOMYCOSIS

What is blastomycosis, and how does an animal get this disease?

Blastomycosis is a fungal disease caused by *Blastomyces dermatitidis*. This fungus most commonly infects humans and animals through the respiratory tract. After spores are inhaled, they settle in the small airways and begin to reproduce. Subsequent to this, the organism spreads throughout the body to involve many organs. Infrequently, infection occurs through inoculation of an open wound.

Although researchers in human medicine have been mostly unsuccessful in reliably isolating the organism from the environment, it does appear that both humans and animals become infected from particular environmental sources, probably the soil. In the United States, the disease is most prevalent in the warm, moist environment found in the Ohio and Mississippi River valleys. It is very common in the Southeastern United States.

What can I do to rid the environment of the fungal organism?

Nothing. The organism is ubiquitous, which means it lives everywhere.

What are the signs of this disease?

The fungus seems to have preferences for certain body systems, although it is usually disseminated (spread) throughout the entire body. Fever, depression, weight loss, and anorexia are common. Draining lesions on the skin are seen in most cases. Some degree of respiratory distress is present in advanced cases. Blindness may occur suddenly because the eyes are frequently involved. Lameness, orchitis (testicular inflammation), seizures, coughing, enlarged lymph nodes, and a variety of other signs are reported.

How is blastomycosis diagnosed?

The only tests which conclusively diagnose blastomycosis are cytology and histopathology. Cytology, the microscopic study of cells, may be performed in the veterinarian's office on some of the fluid draining from an open wound or aspirated from a nodule or lymph node. Histopathology is the study of abnormal or damaged cells and tissue architecture; a tissue sample is sent away to a veterinary pathologist. Because the organism is shed in large numbers in the draining lesions, blastomycosis is usually diagnosed in the office with cytology.

Be aware that there is a *screening blood test* (AGID) to determine potential exposure. A positive result on this test does not equate with infection; it only shows exposure to the organism. Many humans and animals have positive screening tests, but this does not mean that they have (or had) blastomycosis.

Can the disease be treated?

Yes, although not all animals will survive. Fortunately, the newest anti-fungal agent being used is well-tolerated by most animals and has relatively few side-effects when compared to the agents being used several years ago. The drug, itraconazole (Sporanox®), is quite expensive. Dogs may require several months of therapy. The drug is given once daily with food.

How do I know if my animal will survive?

There is no way to determine this before treatment is begun, although an animal in poor condition and with advanced disease is less likely to survive. For many, the critical period comes in the first 24 - 72 hours when the drug takes effect and the fungi begin to die. The lungs harbor a large number of organisms. A severe inflammatory response may occur as treatment takes effect and the organisms begin to die in the lungs. Respiratory distress may be a significant problem in the first few days of therapy. The animal's chest will be X-rayed prior to therapy to determine the presence and significance of a fungal pneumonia, although the chest X-ray cannot predict the outcome of treatment.

Relapse of infection is more common when the organism involves the nervous system, the testicles, or the eyes. Many drugs have difficulty penetrating the natural barriers of the nervous system, and infections here are hard to treat. Male dogs may need to be castrated to remove this potential source of organisms. For similar reasons, one or both eyes may be removed, especially if the animal has already been blinded by the disease. The risk of relapse is very real with this disease, even though treatment appears successful.

Am I at risk of infection from my animal?

Studies on the fungus have found that once an animal is infected, the organism enters a different form or phase; this does not appear to be infectious to other animals or to humans. However, common sense would dictate that strict hygiene should be followed in handling the draining lesions. Thorough hand-washing should follow contact with these animals.

The infected pet does not need to be segregated from the owner or other household pets. The true risk of infection to others probably comes from sharing the same environment which infected the pet (i.e., soil, etc.). Because the *Blastomyces* organism may be harbored near your home, we would recommend that you advise your family physician of your pet's diagnosis. Also, if anyone in your family falls into one of the following categories, we would recommend that you consult with your physician:

- Infants or small children
- Transplant patients
- Chemotherapy patients
- HIV/AIDS
- Elderly family members
- Anyone with a known immuno-suppressed state

BLOAT (GDV)

What is meant by the term " Bloat" in dogs?

This is a term that is synonymous with the more scientific term "Gastric Dilatation/Volvulus." It is often called GDV. That means that a dog's stomach distends with air to the point that it goes into shock and may die. *Dilatation* means that the stomach is distended with air, but it is located in the abdomen in its correct place. *Volvulus* means that the distention is associated with a twisting of the stomach on its longitudinal axis.

How or why does this occur?

We really do not know the answer to either of those questions. Original theories suggested that it occurred when a dog ate a large meal of dry food and then drank a lot of water. The water caused the dry food to swell. At the same time, the dog was supposed to be engaged in strenuous exercise that included running and jumping. That resulted in the dog's stomach twisting on itself as the heavy organ was jostled about in the abdomen. Although that is the most common explanation given, there is no scientific evidence to support this theory. In most dogs experiencing GDV, the stomach is not excessively full of dry food and the dog has not recently engaged in strenuous exercise. The most current theory is that the stomach's contractions lose their regular rhythm and trap air in the stomach; this can cause the twisting event. However, the sequence of events for most cases defies a good explanation.

How is it diagnosed?

The first step in diagnosis is to determine if the correct breed is involved. This condition almost always occurs in deep-chested dogs of large breeds. Some of the more commonly affected breeds include Great Danes, Irish Setters, German Shepherds, and Afghan Hounds. The next step is to establish that the stomach is distended with air. An enlarged stomach will cause the body wall to protrude prominently, especially on the dog's left side. The swelling will be very firm and obvious enough to see across the room. Occasionally, this distention is not very apparent. This occurs in dogs which have a large portion of the stomach up under the rib cage. In most cases, however, the owner is able to detect the distention. A dog which experiences significant pain will be very depressed. It may lie in what is commonly called a "praying position" with the front legs drawn fully forward. This should occur quickly, within two to three hours at the most. The presence of a rapidly developing distended abdomen in a large breed dog is enough evidence to make a tentative diagnosis of GDV. A radiograph (x-ray) is used to confirm the diagnosis of dilatation. It can also identify the presence of volvulus, in most cases.

What happens when the stomach is distended with air?

The first major life-threatening event that occurs is shock. This occurs because the distended stomach puts pressure on the large veins in the abdomen that carry blood back to the heart. Without proper return of blood, the output of blood from the heart is diminished, and the tissues are deprived of blood and oxygen.

The reduced blood output from the heart and the high pressure within the cavity of the stomach cause the stomach wall to be deprived of adequate circulation. If the blood supply is not restored quickly, the wall of the stomach begins to die; the wall may rupture. If volvulus occurs, the spleen's blood supply will also be impaired. This organ is attached to the stomach wall and shares some large blood vessels. When the stomach twists, the spleen is also rotated to an abnormal position and its vessels are compressed. When the stomach is distended, digestion stops. This results in the accumulation of toxins that are normally removed from the intestinal tract. These toxins activate several chemicals which cause inflammation, and the toxins are absorbed into circulation. This causes problems with the blood clotting factors so that inappropriate clotting occurs within blood vessels. This is called disseminated intravascular coagulation (DIC) and is usually fatal.

What is done to save the dog's life?

There are several important steps that must be taken quickly.

- Shock must be treated with administration of large quantities of intravenous fluids. They must be given quickly; some dogs require more than one intravenous line.
- Pressure must be removed from within the stomach. This may be done with a tube that is passed from the mouth to the stomach. Another method is to insert a large bore needle through the skin into the stomach.
- A third method is to make an incision through the skin into the stomach and to temporarily suture the opened stomach to the skin. The last method is usually done when the dog's condition is so grave that anesthesia and abdominal surgery is not possible.
- The stomach must be returned to its proper position. This requires abdominal surgery which can be risky because of the dog's condition.
- The stomach wall must be inspected for areas that may have lost its blood supply. Although this is a very bad prognostic sign, the devitalized area(s) of the stomach should be surgically removed.
- The stomach must be attached to the abdominal wall (gastropexy) to prevent recurrence of GDV.
- Although this is not always successful, this procedure greatly reduces the likelihood of recurrence.
- Abnormalities in the rhythm of the heart (arrhythmias) must be diagnosed and treated. Severe arrhythmias can become life-threatening at the time of surgery and for several days after surgery. An electrocardiogram (ECG) is the best method for monitoring the heart's rhythm.

What is the survival rate?

This will largely be determined by the severity of the distention, the degree of shock, how quickly treatment is begun, and the presence of other diseases, especially those involving the heart. Approximately 60 to 70% of the dogs will survive.

What can be done to prevent it from occurring again?

The most effective means of prevention is gastropexy, the surgical attachment of the stomach to the body wall. This will not prevent dilatation (bloat), but it will prevent volvulus in most cases. Various dietary and exercise restrictions have been used, but none of these have proven value.

BONE DISEASES OF PUPPIES AND GROWING DOGS

I have a young dog with a lameness that has been present for several days. Could this be serious?

There are many causes of lameness. Most of these are relatively minor and are within the body's healing capability. However, there are also causes that are not self-limiting and, if not treated promptly, may result in permanent lameness and/or arthritis. The large breeds of dogs (i.e., those whose adult weight is over 60 pounds) have several bone diseases that occur during the period of rapid growth (up to 2 years of age). Because of the possibility of permanent lameness resulting, we recommend an accurate diagnosis if a lameness lasts more than 2 weeks. In order to get a diagnosis, a set of radiographs (x-rays) is made of the affected leg(s). In some cases, the opposite (normal) leg is radiographed for comparative purposes. Several radiographs are necessary in order to get an accurate look at various bones and joints. This will require a short-acting anesthetic in order to get the positioning that is necessary.

What diseases are likely?

The following diseases will be considered by your veterinarian upon examining radiographs:

- **Rear legs only**

  Hip Dysplasia: an improper formation of the hip joint(s). This is a ball and socket joint. Hip dysplasia results in the ball not being round, the socket not being deep, and the two not fitting together well. Hip dysplasia has several contributing causes, but the primary cause is genetic. A dog of the high-risk breeds for hip dysplasia should not be bred before radiographs of the hips are taken. There are several choices of treatment depending on the severity. Some involve medication; some require surgery.

- **Front legs only**

  Elbow Dysplasia: a lack of fusion of the top of the ulna at the rear point of the elbow. This is more properly termed ununited anconeal process. When this part of the ulna does not fuse, the joint is unstable and is quickly subject to arthritis. Treatment requires surgery.

  Fractured Coronoid Process: the fracture of a small process (protrusion) on the radius within the elbow joint. When this process fractures, pain and joint instability result. Unless surgery is done promptly after the fracture occurs, return to normal use of the leg is unlikely.

- **Front or rear legs**

  Panosteitis: an inflammation on the surface of the long bones. This is also termed "long bone" or "growing pains." This may occur in more than one bone at a time and may cause lameness in one bone or leg and then another. It is self-limiting but may recur until rapid growth is over. The pain may be relieved with several types of medication.

  Osteochondritis dissecans (OD): a defect in the smooth cartilage surface within one or more of several joints. It may affect the shoulder (most commonly), the elbow, the hip, the knee, or the stifle. Some of these defects may heal with confinement of the dog for several weeks. However, most do not and a few may result in a piece of cartilage breaking off and floating freely in the joint. This disease causes pain which varies in its severity. It is best treated with surgery to remove the defective cartilage.

  Hypertrophic Osteodystrophy (HOD): an inflammation in the growth plates of the long bones. It usually causes swelling and pain in the joints. These may lead to fever and loss of appetite. It is self-limiting in most dogs with no permanent damage. However, some dogs may suffer permanent damage to the growth plates resulting in deformed legs. Treatment is with medication to relieve the pain and suppress the inflammation.

Breeding dogs and raising puppies can be an extremely rewarding experience or it may produce frustration and failure. The following information is provided in order to increase your chances of success.

How often does a female dog come into heat?

The female dog comes into heat (estrus) about every 6 months, although very large breeds of dogs may cycle every 8 - 10 months. The heat period lasts about 3 weeks.

What are the signs of heat?

The most notable sign of heat is vaginal bleeding. This begins about the end of the first week of estrus and lasts for about 10 - 14 days. Another consistent sign is swelling of the vulva. During estrus male dogs will be attracted to her.

What should I do to be sure that a breeding is accomplished successfully?

Male dogs are more successful breeders when the environment is familiar. Therefore, it is preferable to take the female to the male's home for breeding. The timing for breeding is critical. The most fertile time is considered the 10th through the 14th days of estrus; however, some dogs will be fertile as early as the 3rd day and as late as the 18th day.

Are there tests to determine when to breed?

There are two tests that are used for this purpose. The first is a microscopic examination of vaginal cells to detect changes to cell appearance and numbers. This has been used for many years and is reasonably reliable. A newer test determines changes in the progesterone level in the blood. This test is more accurate, but is more expensive than monitoring vaginal cells. It is used for dogs that have a history of unsuccessful breeding or for very valuable breeders.

What should I expect during my dog's pregnancy?

Pregnancy, also called the gestation period, ranges from 60 to 67 days, averaging 63 days. Most dogs deliver (whelp) between days 63 and 65. The only way to accurately determine the stage of pregnancy is to count days from the time of breeding. If possible, the breeding date(s) should be recorded. The mother should be examined 3 weeks after breeding to confirm her pregnancy.

A pregnant dog should be fed a puppy formulation of a premium brand of dog food for the duration of the pregnancy and through the nursing period. These diets are generally available through veterinary hospitals or pet stores. Puppy diets provide all the extra nutrition needed for the mother and her litter. If the mother is eating one of these diets, no calcium, vitamin, or mineral supplements are needed. The puppy formulation is necessary to provide the extra nutrients for pregnancy and nursing. During pregnancy, the mother's food consumption will often reach 1.5 times her level before pregnancy. By the end of the nursing period, it may exceed 2 times the pre-pregnancy amount. Do not withhold food; increasing the number of feedings per day is helpful in allowing her to eat enough for her needs and those of the puppies.

What should I do to prepare for whelping?

From the time of breeding, many dogs show behavioral changes. Most develop an unusually sweet and loving disposition and demand more affection and attention. However, some may become uncharacteristically irritable. Some experience a few days of vomiting ("morning sickness"), followed by the development of a ravenous appetite which persists throughout the pregnancy. During the latter stages of pregnancy, the expectant mother begins to look for a secure place for delivery. Many become uncomfortable being alone and will cling closely to the owner. At the onset of labor, many nervously seek a place to make the "nest" or birthing place. If the dog is attached to her owner, she will not want to be left alone at the time of delivery. If left alone, she may delay delivery until the owner returns.

Prior to the time of delivery, a whelping box should be selected and placed in a secluded place, such as a closet or a dark corner. The box should be large enough for the dog to move around freely, but have low enough sides so that she can see out and so you can reach inside to give assistance, if needed. The bottom of the box should be lined with several layers of newspapers. These provide a private hiding place for the expectant and delivering mother and will absorb the birthing fluids. The upper, soiled layers may be removed with minimal interruption to the mother and her newborn puppies.

What happens during labor and delivery?

Most dogs experience delivery without complications; however, first-time mothers should be attended by their owners until at least one or two puppies are born. If these are born quickly and without assistance, further attendance may not be necessary, although it is desirable. If the owner elects to leave, care should be taken so that the dog does not try to follow and leave the whelping box. The signs of impending labor generally include nervousness and panting. The dog will often stop eating during the last 24 hours before labor. She will also usually have a drop in rectal temperature below 100°F (37.8°C). The temperature drop may occur intermittently for several days prior to delivery, but it will usually be constant for the last 24 hours.

Delivery times will vary. Dogs having slim heads, such as Shelties, Collies, and Dobermans, may complete delivery in one to two hours. Dogs having large, round heads generally require longer delivery times. English Bulldogs, Boston Terriers, and Pekinese puppies tend to have sizable heads that make delivery more difficult. It is not unusual for these breeds to rest an hour or more between each puppy. Rarely, a dog may deliver one or two puppies, then have labor stop for as long as twenty-four hours before the remainder of the litter is born. However, if labor does not resume within a few hours after the delivery of the first puppies, examination by a veterinarian is advised. If labor is interrupted for twenty-four hours or more, veterinary assistance should definitely be obtained.

Puppies are usually born head first; however, breech presentations, in which the puppy is delivered tail-end first, occur about 40% of the time and are also considered normal. Each puppy is enclosed in a sac that is part of the placenta ("afterbirth"). The placentas usually pass after the puppies are born. However, any that do not pass will disintegrate and pass within 24 - 48 hours after delivery. It is normal for the mother to eat the placenta.

If the delivery proceeds normally, a few contractions will discharge the puppy; it should exit the birth canal within ten minutes of being visible. Following delivery, the mother should lick the newborn's face. She will then proceed to wash it and toss it about. Her tongue is used to tear the sac and expose the mouth and nose. This vigorous washing stimulates circulation, causing the puppy to cry and begin breathing; it also dries the newborn's haircoat. The mother will sever the umbilical cord by chewing it about 3/4 to 1 inch (1.9 to 2.5 cm) from the body. Next, she will eat the placenta.

If the puppy or a fluid-filled bubble is partially visible from the vagina, the owner should assist delivery. A dampened gauze or thin wash cloth can be used to break the bubble and grasp the head or feet. When a contraction occurs, firm traction should be applied in a downward (i.e., toward her rear feet) direction. If reasonable traction is applied without being able to remove the puppy, or if the mother cries intensely during this process, the puppy is probably lodged. A veterinarian's assistance should be sought without delay.

It is normal for the mother to remove the placental sac and clean the puppies; however, first-time mothers may be bewildered by the experience and hesitate to do so. If the sac is not removed within a few minutes after delivery, the puppy will suffocate, so you should be prepared to intervene. The puppy's face should be wiped with a damp wash cloth or gauze to remove the sac and allow breathing. Vigorous rubbing with a soft, warm towel will stimulate circulation and dry the hair. The umbilical cord should be tied with cord (i.e., sewing thread, dental floss) and cut with clean scissors. The cord should be tied snugly and cut about 1/2 inch (1.3 cm) from the body so it is unlikely to be pulled off as the puppy moves around the whelping box.

Newborn puppies may aspirate fluid into the lungs, as evidenced by a raspy noise during respiration. This fluid can be removed by the following procedure. First, the puppy should be held in the palm of your hand. The puppy's face should be cradled between the first two fingers. The head should be held firmly with this hand, and the body should be held firmly with the other. Next, a downward swing motion with the hands should make the puppy gasp. Gravity will help the fluid and mucus to flow out of the lungs. This process may be tried several times until the lungs sound clear. The tongue is a reliable indicator of successful respiration. If the puppy is getting adequate oxygen, it will appear pink to red. A bluish colored tongue indicates insufficient oxygen to the lungs, signaling that the swinging procedure should be repeated.

It may be helpful to have a smaller, clean, dry box lined with a warm towel for the newborn puppies. (A towel can be warmed in a microwave oven.) After the puppy is stable and the cord has been tied, it should be placed in the incubator box while the mother is completing delivery. Warmth is essential so a heating pad or hot water bottle may be placed in the box, or a heat lamp may be placed nearby. If a heating pad is used, it should be placed on the low setting and covered with a towel to prevent overheating. A hot water bottle should be covered with a towel. Remember, the newborn puppies may be unable to move away from the heat source. Likewise, caution should also be exercised when using a heat lamp.

Once delivery is completed, the soiled newspapers should be removed from the whelping box. The box should be lined with soft bedding prior to the puppies' return. The mother should accept the puppies readily and recline for nursing.

The mother and her litter should be examined by a veterinarian within 24 hours after the delivery is completed. This visit is to check the mother for complete delivery, and to check the newborn puppies. The mother may receive an injection to contract the uterus and stimulate milk production.

The mother will have a bloody vaginal discharge for 3 - 7 days following delivery. If it continues for longer than one week, she should be examined by a veterinarian for possible problems.

What happens if my dog has trouble delivering her puppies?

Although most dogs deliver without need for assistance, problems do arise which require the attention of a veterinarian. Professional assistance should be sought if any of the following occur:

- Twenty minutes of intense labor occurs without a puppy being delivered.
- Ten minutes of intense labor occurs when a puppy or a fluid-filled bubble is visible in the birth canal.
- The mother experiences sudden depression or marked lethargy.
- The mother's body temperature exceeds 103°F (39.4°C) (via a rectal thermometer).
- Fresh blood discharges from the vagina for more than 10 minutes.

Difficulty delivering (dystocia) may be managed with or without surgery. The condition of the mother, size of the litter, and size of the puppies are factors used in making that decision.

Is premature delivery a likely problem?

Occasionally, a mother will deliver a litter several days premature. The puppies may be small, thin, and have little or no hair. It is possible for them to survive, but they require an enormous amount of care, since they are subject to chilling and are frequently very weak and unable to swallow. Some may be able to nurse but are so weak that they must be held next to the mother. Puppies that do not nurse can be fed with a small syringe, bottle, or stomach tube. The equipment and instructions for these procedures are available from a veterinarian. Premature puppies must be kept warm. The mother can provide sufficient radiant heat from her body if she will stay close to them. If she refuses, heat can be provided with a heat lamp, heating pad, or hot water bottle. Excessive heat can be just as harmful as chilling, so any form of artificial heat must be controlled. The temperature in the box should be maintained at 85 to 90°F (29.4° - 32.2°C), but the box should be large enough so the puppies can move away from the heat if it becomes uncomfortable.

Is it likely that one or more puppies will be stillborn?

It is not uncommon for one or two puppies in a litter to be stillborn. Sometimes, a stillborn puppy will disrupt labor, resulting in dystocia. At other times, the dead puppy will be born normally. Although there is always a cause for this occurrence, it is often not easily determined without an autopsy that includes cultures and the submission of tissues to a pathologist. This is only recommended in special circumstances.

What do I do to care for the newborn puppies?

The mother will spend most of her time with the puppies during the next few days. The puppies need to be kept warm and to nurse frequently; they should be checked every few hours to make certain that they are warm and well fed. The mother should be checked to make certain that she is producing adequate milk.

If the mother does not stay in the box, the puppies' temperatures must be monitored. If the puppies are cold, supplemental heating should be provided. During the first four days of life, the newborns' box should be maintained at 85 - 90°F (29.4 - 32.2°C). The temperature may gradually be decreased to 80°F (26.7°C) by the seventh to tenth day and to 72°F (22.2°C) by the end of the fourth week. If the litter is large, the temperature need not be as high. As puppies huddle together, their body heat provides additional warmth.

If the mother feels the puppies are in danger or if there is too much light, she may become anxious. Placing a sheet or cloth over most of the top of the box to obscure much of the light may resolve the problem. An enclosed box is also a solution. Some dogs, especially first-time mothers, are more anxious than others. Such dogs may attempt to hide their young, even from her owner. Moving from place to place may continue and will endanger the puppies if they are placed in a cold or drafty location. Dogs with this behavior should be caged in a secluded area. This type of mother has also been known to kill her puppies as a means of "protecting" them from danger.

What are the signs that the puppies are not doing well and what do I do?

Puppies should eat or sleep 90% of the time during the first 2 weeks. If they are crying during or after eating, they are usually becoming ill or are not getting adequate milk. A newborn puppy is very susceptible to infections and can die within 24 hours. If excessive crying occurs, the mother and entire litter should be examined by a veterinarian promptly.

When the milk supply is inadequate, supplemental feeding one to three times per day is recommended and should be performed on any litter with 5+ puppies. There are several commercial formulae available that are made to supply the needs of puppies. They should be warmed to 95 - 100°F (35 - 37.8°C) before feeding. It is useful to test the temperature before feeding. Drop some warmed formula onto your forearm. It should be about the same temperature. An alternative is canned goats' milk that is available in most grocery stores. The commercial products have directions concerning feeding amounts. If the puppies are still nursing from their mother, the amounts recommended will be excessive. Generally, 1/3 to 1/2 of the listed amount should be the daily goal. Supplemental feeding may be continued until the puppies are old enough to eat puppy food.

If the mother does not produce milk or her milk becomes infected, the puppies will also cry. If this occurs, the entire litter could die within 24 to 48 hours. Total replacement feeding, using the mentioned products, or adopting the puppies to another nursing mother is usually necessary. If replacement feeding is chosen, the amounts of milk listed on the product should be fed. Puppies less than 2 weeks of age should be fed every 3 - 4 hours. Puppies 2 - 4 weeks of age do well with feedings every 6 - 8 hours. Weaning should begin at 3 - 4 weeks of age.

What should I expect during the puppies' first few weeks of life?

For the first month of life, puppies require very little care from the owner because their mother will feed and care for them. They are born with their eyes closed, but they will open in 7 to 14 days. If swelling or bulging is noted under the eyelids, they should be opened gently. A cotton ball dampened with warm water may be used to assist opening the lids. If the swelling is due to infection, pus will exit the open eyelids and should be treated as prescribed by a veterinarian. If the eyes have not opened within 14 days of age, they should be opened by a veterinarian. Puppies should be observed for their rate of growth. They should double their birth weight in about one week. At two weeks of age, puppies should be alert and trying to stand. At three weeks, they generally try to climb out of their box. At four weeks, all of the puppies should be able to walk, run, and play.

Puppies should begin eating solid food about 3 1/2 to 4 1/2 weeks of age. Initially, one of the milk replacers or cow's milk diluted 50:50 with water should be placed in a flat saucer. The puppies' noses should be dipped into the milk 2 or 3 times per day until they begin to lap; this usually takes 1 - 3 days. Next, canned puppy food should be placed in the milk until it is soggy. As the puppies lap the milk, they will also ingest the food. The amount of milk should be decreased daily until they are eating the canned food with little or no moisture added; this should occur by 4 to 6 weeks of age.

I have heard of milk fever. What exactly is it?

Eclampsia, or milk fever, is a depletion of calcium from the mother due to heavy milk production. It generally occurs when the puppies are 3 - 5 weeks old (just before weaning) and most often to mothers with large litters. The mother has muscle spasms resulting in rigid legs, spastic movements, and heavy panting. This can be fatal in 30 - 60 minutes, so a veterinarian should be consulted immediately.

Do puppies need a special diet?

Diet is extremely important for a growing puppy. There are many commercial foods specially formulated for puppies. These foods meet their unique nutritional requirements and should be fed until 12 - 18 months of age. Puppy foods are available in dry and canned formulations. Dry foods are less expensive and can be left in the bowl for the puppy to eat at will. Canned foods offer a change and are just as nutritious.

- We recommend that you buy FOOD FORMULATED FOR PUPPIES. Adult formulations are not recommended since they do not provide the nutrition required for a puppy. Advertisements tend to promote taste rather than nutrition, so be careful that their influence on purchasing habits is not detrimental to your dog. Generic foods should be avoided. Table food is not recommended; although often more appealing than dog food, balanced nutrition is usually compromised.

- We recommend that you buy NAME BRAND FOOD. It is generally a good idea to avoid generic brands of food. We recommend that you only buy food which has the AAFCO (American Association of Feed Control Officials) certification. Usually, you can find this information very easily on the food label. AAFCO is an organization which oversees the entire pet food industry. It does not endorse any particular food, but it will tell you if the food has met the minimum requirements for nutrition which are set by the industry. Most commercial pet foods will have the AAFCO label. In Canada, look for foods aproved by the Canadian Veterinary Medical Association (CVMA).

When should vaccinations begin?

Puppies are provided some immunity to canine diseases from their mother before and shortly after birth. Some of the mother's antibodies cross the placenta and enter the puppies' circulation, but most antibodies are provided in the mother's milk, particularly the first milk or colostrum. These "maternal antibodies" protect the puppies against the diseases to which the mother is immune. This explains why it is desirable to booster the mother's vaccinations within a few months prior to breeding.

Although very protective, maternal antibodies last for only a few weeks; after this time, the puppy becomes susceptible to disease. The duration of the maternal antibodies is quite variable depending on several factors but, in general, the vaccination program should be started at about 6 to 8 weeks of age. Puppies should be vaccinated against distemper, hepatitis, leptospirosis, parainfluenza virus, parvovirus, coronavirus, and rabies. Other vaccines are also available for certain situations, and will be discussed at the time of the first visit for vaccinations.

Maternal antibodies are passed in the mother's milk only during the first 1 - 3 days after delivery. If, for any reason, the puppies do not nurse during this important period of time, their vaccinations should begin about 2 to 4 weeks of age, depending on likely disease exposure. Your veterinarian can make specific recommendations for each particular situation.

Do all puppies have worms?

Intestinal parasites ("worms") are common in puppies. Symptoms include a general poor condition, chronic soft or bloody stools, loss of appetite, a pot-bellied appearance, loss of luster of the haircoat, and weight loss. Some parasites are transmitted from the mother to her offspring and others are carried by fleas. Some are transmitted through the stool of an infected dog. Very few of these parasites are visible in the stool, so their eggs must be detected by the veterinarian with a microscope.

A microscopic examination of the feces will reveal the eggs of most of these parasites. Generally this test should be performed at the time of the first vaccinations. However, it may be performed as early as 3 weeks of age if a parasite problem is suspected. Treatment is based on the type of parasites found although some veterinarians elect to treat all puppies because they know that fecal tests can be falsely negative. Your veterinarian should be consulted for specific recommendations for your puppies.

CESAREAN SECTION POST-OPERATIVE INSTRUCTIONS

A cesarean section is major surgery to remove puppies from the uterus. Most dogs recover quickly from this procedure; however, if your dog was in labor for several hours before surgery was performed, her recovery will be slower, and she will need extra attention and help with her litter.

What should I expect during the mother's recovery period?

The mother has been given an anesthetic that is eliminated from her body rather quickly. Most dogs are raising their heads about the time they arrive at home. Complete recovery from anesthetic may take 2 - 6 hours, depending on the mother's physical condition at the time of surgery and her age. During the recovery period, she must be restrained in such a way that she does not fall and hurt herself or roll over and crush the puppies. The puppies should not be left alone with her until she is completely awake and coordinated. The mother should be interested in eating within a few hours after she is completely awake. Allow her to eat and drink all that she wants, being careful that she does not overload her stomach. This can result in vomiting. Her food intake at this time should be about 1½ times her food intake before she became pregnant. By the third or fourth week of nursing, her food intake may be 2 to 2½ times normal. The mother's temperature may rise 1 - 2°F (0.5 - 1°C) above normal for the first 1 - 3 days after delivery, then it should return to the normal range. The normal range is 100 - 102°F (37.8 - 38.9°C). Your dog should not be given aspirin because it may aggravate bleeding. However, acetaminophen is appropriate at a dose of 325 mg (one regular strength tablet) per 50lb (23kg). If the mother's temperature goes above 104°F (40°C), she and her litter should be examined by a veterinarian for the presence of serious complications.

When should the puppies begin to nurse?

The puppies should be ready to nurse as soon as you arrive at home. Although the mother will not be awake enough to handle the nursing alone, it is still possible for you to assist the process by making her lie still so the puppies can nurse. If the mother does not have any milk at first, you may supplement the puppies for the first day or two. There are several good commercial canine milk replacers available. Nursing bottles are available, made in the appropriate size for tiny mouths. The following formula may be used for a day or two if the other products are not available:

1 cup (240 mL) milk + 1 tablespoon (15 mL) corn oil + 1 pinch of salt + 3 egg yolks (no whites). Blend together until uniform. It should be fed at the rate of 1 oz (30 cc or 30 mL) per 1/4 lb of puppy weight PER 24 HOURS. That amount should be divided into 3 - 5 feedings. The average newborn, small breed puppy weighs 1/4 lb (100 g) at birth.

Another alternative is canned goat's milk that is available in most grocery stores. It should be fed at the above amounts. Although it is desirable for puppies to begin nursing immediately, a healthy newborn can survive nicely for up to 12 hours without nursing. However, if the newborn is weak, dehydrated, or chilled, nourishment must be given very soon.

How warm should we keep the room where the puppies are?

A newborn puppy is not able to regulate its body temperature very well. As long as the puppies stay near their mother, the room temperature is not too critical. However, if they are not with their mother, the room temperature should be between 85 and 90°F (29.4 and 32.2°C). If the litter is kept outside, chilling or overheating is much more likely to occur. The newborns should be kept inside the house or the garage, if possible.

Is a bloody vaginal discharge normal?

A bloody vaginal discharge is normal for 3 - 7 days following birth. It may be quite heavy for the first 1 - 3 days, then it should begin to diminish. If it continues for longer than one week, the mother should be checked for the presence of infection. If she was spayed at the time of the surgery, there should be no vaginal discharge.

What does it mean if the puppies are crying frequently?

Puppies should sleep or be nursing 90% of the time. If they are crying or whining, something is likely to be wrong. Uterine infections, inadequate milk, poor-quality milk, and infected milk are the most likely causes. The entire litter can die within 24 hours if one of these occurs. If you are not comfortable with the way the litter is doing, the puppies and the mother should be examined by a veterinarian.

When are her stitches removed?

The stitches may or may not need to be removed, depending on the type of suture material used. As a general rule, if the stitches are visible, they will have to be removed. Removal should occur at 10 - 14 days after surgery.

When should the puppies be weaned?

Weaning should begin when the puppies are about 3½ weeks old. The first step is to place a 50:50 mixture of water and milk replacer or cow's milk in a flat saucer. The puppies' noses should be dipped in this mixture 2 - 3 times per day until they begin to lap. Once lapping begins, a puppy-type canned food should be crumbled in the water/milk mixture. As they begin to eat the solid food, the water/milk mixture should be reduced until they are eating only the solid food. Once they are eating solid food (about 5 - 6 weeks of age), they may be placed in their new home.

When are the puppies treated for worms?

Puppies can be treated for worms when they are 3 and 6 weeks of age. It is important that accurate weights are obtained for the puppies so that the proper dose of medication can be used.

When should vaccinations begin?

First vaccinations typically begin at 6 - 8 weeks of age. If your puppies were not able to nurse during the first 3 days of life, they will not have received proper immunity from their mother. In this situation, vaccinations should begin about 2 weeks of age.

COCCIDIOSIS

What is coccidiosis?

Coccidiosis is an infection with a one-celled organism; these organisms are classified as protozoa and are called coccidia. Coccidia are not worms; they are microscopic parasites which live within cells of the intestinal lining. Because they live in the intestinal tract and commonly cause diarrhea, they are often confused with worms.

How did my dog become infected with coccidia?

Oocysts (immature coccidia) are passed in the stool of the dog. They remain in the environment and eventually sporulate (mature) into a more developed oocyst which can infect the dog again. Other dogs, cats, or mice may also become infected. This process can occur in as little as 6 hours, but it usually takes 7 - 10 days. If the sporulated oocysts are swallowed, they mature in the dog's intestine to complete the life cycle. If the oocysts should be swallowed by a mouse, the dog may also become infected by eating the mouse.

What kinds of problems are caused by coccidial infection?

Most dogs that are infected with coccidia do not have diarrhea or any other clinical signs. When the eggs (oocysts) are found in the stool of a dog without diarrhea, they are generally considered a transient, insignificant finding. However, in puppies and debilitated adult dogs, they may cause severe, watery diarrhea, dehydration, abdominal distress, and vomiting. In severe cases, death may occur.

How is coccidial infection diagnosed?

Coccidiosis is diagnosed by performing a microscopic examination of a stool sample. Since the oocysts are much smaller than the eggs of the intestinal worms, a very careful study must be made. Infection with some of the less common coccidial parasites is diagnosed with a blood test.

How is the coccidial infection treated?

The most common drug used to eliminate coccidia is a sulfa-type antibiotic. It is given for 10 - 14 days. Other drugs are also used if diarrhea and dehydration occur. If the sulfa-type drug is not effective, others are available. Reinfection of dogs is common so environmental disinfection is important. The use of chlorine bleach, one cup in a gallon of water (500 mL in 4 liters), is effective if the surfaces and premises can be safely treated with it.

Are the coccidial parasites of my dog infectious to humans?

The most common coccidia found in dogs do not have any affect on humans. However, less common types of coccidia are potentially infectious to humans. One parasite, called *Cryptosporidium*, may be carried by dogs or cats and may be transmitted to people. This parasite has also been found in public water supplies in some major cites.

> Coccidial parasites pose a health risk for immuno-suppressed humans (i.e., AIDS patients, those taking immune suppressing drugs, cancer patients, or the elderly).

Good hygiene and proper disposal of dog feces are important in minimizing risk of transmission of all canine parasites to humans. Although there is risk of the dog transmitting these two particular parasites to humans, it does not warrant removing the dog from the household except in very rare instances.

COLLAPSED TRACHEA

What is a collapsed trachea?

The trachea, also known as the windpipe, is an important structure which connects the throat to the lungs. It serves the purpose of directing air into the respiratory tract. The normal trachea is tubular. It maintains its shape because of a series of rings made of cartilage. These rings do not completely encircle the trachea. Instead, they go from the 2 o'clock to 10 o'clock positions. The remainder of the trachea is composed of a flexible membrane that joins the ends of the cartilage rings. When the cartilage rings are flattened from the top to the bottom, the trachea is said to be collapsed. Rapid inhalation of air can cause the trachea to flatten and make it difficult for air to enter the lungs.

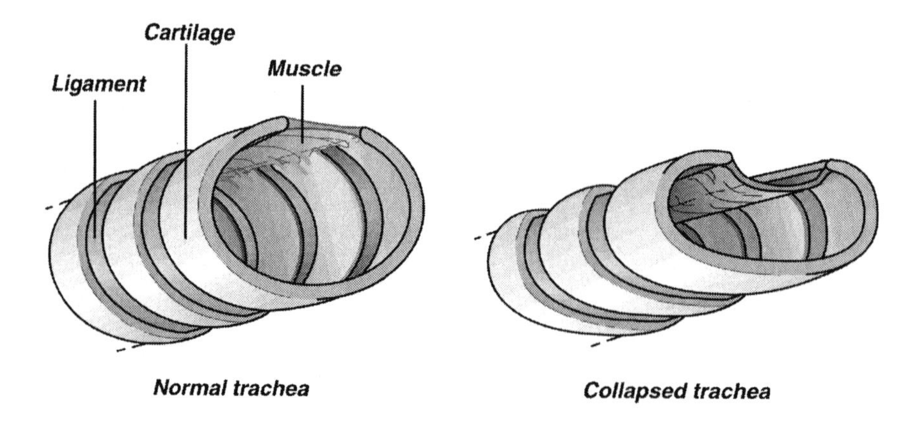

Normal trachea *Collapsed trachea*

Why does it happen?

We do not completely understand how this condition develops. However, we know that these dogs have an abnormality in the chemical makeup of their tracheal rings. The rings loose their stiffness so they are not able to retain their circular shape. We also know that it occurs in certain breeds of dogs, notably Chihuahuas, Pomeranians, Shih Tzus, Lhasa Apsos, Toy Poodles, and Yorkshire Terriers. Because of that, we suspect that there is a genetic factor involved.

What are the clinical signs?

The most common clinical sign is a chronic cough. It is often described as dry and harsh and can become quite pronounced. The term "goose honk" is often used to describe it. Coughing is often worse in the daytime and much less at night. The cough may also begin due to excitement, pressure on the trachea (from a leash), or from drinking water or eating.

How is a collapsed trachea diagnosed?

A dog of the breeds listed previously with a chronic cough, especially a "goose honk," should be suspected as having collapsed trachea. Many times, very light pressure placed on the trachea during the physical examination can raise a suspicion of collapsed trachea in a small dog with a persistent dry cough. While the information gained from the physical examination is helpful, other tests are needed to confirm this condition.

Radiographs (x-rays) of the chest can identify the trachea and its shape. However, a collapsed trachea changes its diameter during the respiratory cycle. It is usually collapsed during inhalation and normal during exhalation. Therefore, we attempt to make radiographs during both phases of respiration. This is easy in some dogs and rather difficult in others since dogs are not likely to understand the command, "Take a deep breath and hold it."

Endoscopy is another way to visualize the trachea. An endoscope is a tube that is small enough to insert into the trachea; the operator can see through it and visualize the inside of the trachea. By watching the trachea during inspiration and expiration, abnormal collapsing can be seen. Unfortunately, tracheal endoscopes are expensive and not available at every veterinary hospital.

Isn't coughing also a sign of heart failure?

Yes, it is. Many dogs with collapsed trachea will also have heart disease. Testing that occurs when diagnosing this disease should include chest radiographs (x-rays) so the heart can be evaluated. Treatment for heart disease is not indicated unless it can be demonstrated with some form of testing.

How is it treated?

Collapsed trachea can be treated medically or surgically. Some dogs respond well to bronchodilators and various types of anti-inflammatory drugs. The trachea of these dogs is easily infected, so antibiotics are usually part of the treatment. If obesity is present, weight loss is often beneficial. Excitement and vigorous exercise are likely to cause a relapse, so they should be avoided as much as possible. Some dogs respond well to the medical approach, and others do not. Because medical therapy only treats the symptoms and does not correct the problem, these dogs are always subject to recurrences of coughing and breathing difficulty.

If medical therapy is not successful, the dog should be evaluated for possible surgery. Radiographs and endoscopy are used to determine how much of the trachea is collapsed. If the only abnormal part is that segment between the throat and the point where the trachea enters the chest (the thoracic inlet), surgery may be curative. However, if the segment of the trachea that is within the chest cavity is abnormal, surgery is not likely to be helpful because that part is not accessible to the surgeon.

There are several surgical approaches that have been used. Each approach implants an artificial support device that is secured around or within the trachea. The purpose of the support device is to hold the tracheal rings in their normal, open position. Although some dogs have excellent results and are truly cured of the disease, the outcome is not uniformly successful.

What is a corneal ulcer?

The cornea is the clear, shiny membrane which makes up the surface of the eyeball. It is much like a clear window. To understand a corneal ulcer, you must first understand how the cornea is constructed. The cornea is comprised of three layers. The most superficial layer is the epithelium. Actually, this layer is comprised of many, very thin layers of cells. Below the epithelium is the stroma, and the deepest layer is Descemet's membrane. Because all of these layers of the cornea are clear, it is not possible to see them without special stains which color particular cells and highlight them when looked at with a microscope.

An erosion of a few layers of the epithelium is called a *corneal erosion* or a *corneal abrasion*. A *corneal ulcer* is an erosion through the entire epithelium and into the stroma. If the erosion goes through the epithelium and stroma to the level of Descemet's membrane, a *descemetocele* exists. If Descemet's membrane ruptures, the liquid inside the eyeball leaks out and the eye collapses.

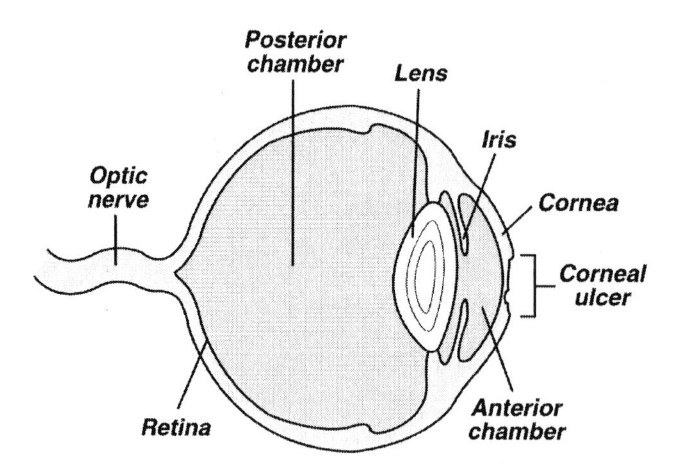

Diagrammatic section of the eye with corneal ulcer.

How does a corneal ulcer occur?

There are several causes for corneal ulcers in dogs. The most common is trauma. An ulcer may result from blunt trauma, such as a dog rubbing its eye on the carpet, or due to a laceration, such as a cat scratch. The second most common cause is chemical burn of the cornea. This may happen when irritating shampoo gets in the eye.

Less common causes of corneal ulcers include bacterial infections, viral infections, and other diseases. These may originate in the eye or develop secondary to disease elsewhere in the body. Examples of other diseases include Epithelial Dystrophy (a softening of the cornea which is inherited in breeds such as the Boxer), Keratoconjunctivitis Sicca (drying of the cornea due to abnormal tear formation), and diseases of the endocrine system (diabetes mellitus, hyperadrenocorticism, and hypothyroidism).

How does a corneal ulcer affect my dog?

A corneal ulcer is very painful. In response to pain, most dogs rub the affected eye with a foot or on the carpet. To protect the eye, they keep the lids tightly closed. Occasionally, there will be a discharge that collects in the corner of the eye or runs down the face.

How is a corneal ulcer diagnosed?

Superficial corneal abrasions are usually not visible. They can be visualized with the use of fluorescein stain. A drop of this stain is placed on the cornea. The dye will adhere to an area of ulceration and is easily visualized with a special black light called a Wood's light. This is the most basic test performed and may be the only test needed if the ulcer is acute and very superficial. If the ulcerated area is chronic or very deep, samples are taken for culture and cell study prior to applying the stain or any other medication.

How is a corneal ulcer treated?

Treatment depends on whether there is a corneal abrasion, corneal ulcer, or descemetocele present. Corneal abrasions generally heal within 3 - 5 days. Medication is used to prevent bacterial infections (antibiotic ophthalmic drops or ointment) and to relieve pain (atropine ophthalmic drops or ointment). Antibiotic drops are only effective for a few minutes so they must be applied frequently; ointments last a bit longer but still require application every few hours. It is suggested that an antibiotic preparation be instilled in the eye 4 to 6 times per day. On the other hand, the effects of atropine last many hours so this drug is only used twice daily.

If a corneal ulcer or descemetocele is present, measures must be taken to protect the eye and to promote healing. Since dogs do not wear eye patches well, surgical techniques are often used to close the eyelids and cover the ulcer or descemetocele. These measures protect the eye for several days, then are reversed so the dog can use the eye again.

Ulcers that do not heal well often have a buildup of dead cells at the ulcer edge. These dead cells prevent normal cells from the corneal surface from sliding over the ulcer edge and filling in the defect. If this appears to be part of the healing problem, the dead cells are removed from the edges of the ulcer before the eyelids are surgically closed. In some cases, removing the dead cells may be all that is needed to start the healing process, so surgical closing of the eyelids may not be necessary.

What if a corneal abrasion really turns out to be a corneal ulcer?

This is a mistake that can happen because there is a judgment call involved in differentiating the two. After 2 - 3 days of treatment, your dog should be re-examined to be sure that healing is progressing properly. If that does not happen, a decision may be made to perform surgery.

Are there any side-effects from the eye medications?

Rarely, a dog will be allergic to an antibiotic that is instilled in the eye. If your dog seems in more pain after the medication is used, discontinue it and contact the veterinarian. A dog with a corneal ulcer has quite a bit of pain in the eye, so it keeps it tightly shut. Atropine is used to relieve that pain. However, atropine also dilates the pupil widely. This means that the dog is very sensitive to light in that eye. Because of the light sensitivity, the eye will be held closed in bright light.

Atropine's effects may last for several days after the drug is discontinued. Do not be alarmed if the pupil stays dilated for several days. Should you accidentally get atropine in your eye, the same prolonged pupillary dilation will occur.

My dog began to drool excessively and paw at its mouth after I administered the eye medications. Is that a reaction?

No. The tear ducts carry tears from the eyes to the back of the nose. The eye medications may go through the tear ducts and eventually get to the throat where they are tasted. Atropine has a very bitter taste which may cause drooling and pawing at the mouth. You are seeing your dog's response to a bad taste, not a drug reaction.

Since a corneal ulcer is painful, can I apply a topical anesthetic to the cornea?

A topical anesthetic is often used to numb the cornea so the diagnostic tests may be performed. However, these drugs are toxic to the corneal epithelium; they prevent proper healing. They are safe for one time use, but they should not be used as part of the treatment.

How do I know when to discontinue medication?

The best way to tell that the cornea has healed is to repeat the fluorescein stain test. This should be done after 5 - 7 days of treatment.

There appear to be some red streaks near the ulcer. Is that normal?

The normal cornea has no blood vessels going through it. However, when a corneal ulcer or descemetocele occurs, the body senses a need to increase its healing capabilities. New blood vessels are created by a process called neovascularization. The new vessels begin at the sclera (the white part of the eye) and course their way to the ulcer.

Neovascularization is a good response because it hastens healing. However, after the ulcer is healed, these vessels remain in the cornea. They are not painful, but they do obstruct vision. Therefore, it is desirable to remove them. This is done with steroid (cortisone) ophthalmic drops or ointment.

Cortisone is used for a few days to several weeks, depending on how many vessels exist.

It is important that steroids not be used in the eye too soon because they will stop healing of a corneal ulcer and may worsen it. Therefore, the fluorescein dye test should be performed before beginning this type of medication. If steroids are used and the eye becomes painful again, discontinue the steroids and have the eye rechecked.

CORONAVIRUS

What is coronavirus disease?

Coronavirus disease is a variable intestinal infection of dogs which is usually transient, but may cause considerable discomfort to the animal for a few days. The cause is a virus of the Coronavirus family (under the electron microscope the virus has a ring of projections which appear like a coronet as seen from above). Different coronaviruses cause infections in many species of animals and birds. People are not affected by the canine coronavirus.

How is the virus transmitted?

Infected dogs usually shed the virus in their feces (and saliva) for 1 to 2 weeks, sometimes much longer. The virus is then ingested from contaminated food bowls, or by direct contact with the infected dog. Crowding and unsanitary conditions favor transmission. The incubation period from ingestion to clinical signs is 1 to 5 days.

What are the signs of coronavirus?

Many infections are inapparent (subclinical) or mild and transient. However occasional infections and outbreaks are more severe particularly in young pups. Mixed infections, for instance with parvovirus may intensify the disease. The diarrhea is typically sudden in onset, with lethargy and decreased appetite. The stool is loose, mushy with a fetid odor and orange tint. It may contain blood, or contain much mucus.

Are there diseases which can be confused with coronavirus?

There are many causes of diarrhea in dogs. Severe cases of coronavirus can be easily confused with parvovirus, and they may coincide. Be sure to see your veterinarian promptly if your dog has diarrhea that does not resolve quickly or is associated with significant lethargy and/or loss of appetite.

Is there any treatment?

There is no specific treatment. Antibiotics are ineffective against viruses, but may be useful in controlling secondary bacterial problems. Withholding food until 24 hours after diarrhea ceases and gradually reintroducing may be sufficient. But any dehydration must be corrected, possibly with intravenous fluids, so that it is advisable to get veterinary attention early.

What about vaccines?

Canine coronavirus vaccines have been developed in recent years, and are becoming more widely used in routine vaccination programs.

I know that knee injuries are common in people. Do they occur in dogs?

The knee joint of the dog is one of the weakest in the body. Just as football players frequently suffer knee injuries, the dog may also be prone to knee injuries.

Why is the knee so likely to be injured?

The knee joint is relatively unstable because there is no interlocking of bones in the joint. Instead, the two main bones, the femur and tibia, are joined with several ligaments. When severe twisting of the joint occurs, the most common injury is a rupture of the anterior cruciate ligament. When it is torn, an instability occurs that allows the bones to move in an abnormal fashion in relation to each other. It is not possible to bear weight on the leg without it collapsing.

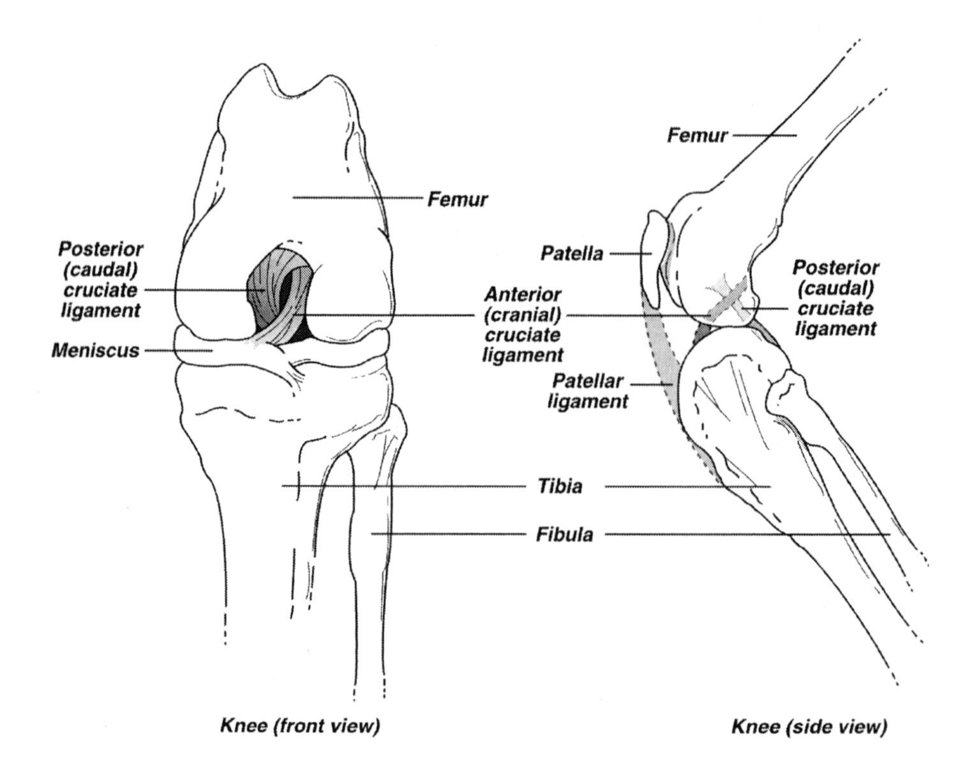

Diagram showing normal relationship of cruciate ligaments to knee joint.

How is it diagnosed?

The most reliable means of diagnosing this injury is to move the femur and tibia in a certain way to demonstrate the instability. This movement is called a "drawer sign." It can usually be demonstrated with the dog awake. If the dog is experiencing severe pain, has very strong leg muscles, or is uncooperative, it may be necessary to use sedation in order to examine the joint thoroughly.

How is it treated?

Correction of this problem requires surgery. A skilled surgeon can fashion a replacement ligament and stabilize the joint so it functions normally or near normally. If surgery is not performed within a few days to a week, arthritic changes will begin that cannot be reversed, even with surgery.

I have heard of torn cartilage. Does this also occur?

Occasionally the injury that causes a ruptured anterior cruciate ligament will also result in tearing of one or both of the menisci or "cartilages." At the time of surgery, these are examined and removed if necessary.

What happens if surgery is not performed?

Occasionally, the dog that has a ruptured cruciate ligament will become sound (will no longer limp) even if surgery is not performed. However, arthritis will usually begin and result in lameness a few months later. That lameness cannot be corrected.

My dog is overweight. Does that relate to this injury?

A special note is appropriate concerning the dog's weight. Obesity or excessive weight can be a strong contributing factor in cruciate rupture. The ligament may become weakened due to carrying too much weight; this causes it to tear easily. Obesity will make the recovery time much longer, and it will make the other knee very susceptible to cruciate rupture. If your dog has a weight problem, there are prescription diets that can be used to assist weight reduction.

CUSHING'S DISEASE

What is Cushing's Disease?

Cushing's Disease is a disease in which the adrenal glands overproduce certain hormones. The correct medical term for this disease is *hyperadrenocorticism.* The adrenal glands produce several vital substances which regulate a variety of body functions and are necessary to sustain life. The most widely known of these substances is cortisol, commonly known as cortisone. Either deficient production or excessive production of these substances may be life-threatening

How does this disease occur?

There are three mechanisms by which this disease can occur. Regardless of the cause, the clinical signs are essentially the same. It is important to identify the cause, however, because the various forms are treated differently and have different prognoses.

- **Iatrogenic**

  Iatrogenic Cushing's Disease means that the excess of cortisone has resulted from excessive administration of cortisone. This may occur from oral or injectable medications. Although the injections or tablets were given for a legitimate medical reason, their excess is now detrimental.

- **Adrenal gland tumor**

  Cushing's Disease may be the result of a benign or malignant tumor of the adrenal gland. If benign, surgical removal cures the disease. If malignant, surgery may help for awhile, but the prognosis is less favorable than for a benign tumor.

- **Pituitary gland tumor**

  The most common cause of Cushing's Disease (85% of all cases) is a tumor of the pituitary gland. The tumor may be either benign or malignant. The tumor causes the pituitary to overproduce a hormone which stimulates the adrenal glands. Excessive cortisone secretion results. The tumor may be either microscopic or quite large. Depending on the size of the tumor, the presence of signs other than Cushing's will be variable. Generally, if the activity of the adrenal gland can be controlled, the dog will live a relatively normal life. Unfortunately, this is sometimes not the case. However, many dogs with this form of Cushing's Disease can live normal lives for many years as long as they take their medication and stay under close medical supervision. Growth of the pituitary tumor would give the patient a less favorable prognosis.

What are the clinical signs?

The most common clinical signs associated with Cushing's Disease are a tremendous increase in appetite, water consumption, and urination. Lethargy, or lack of activity, and a poor hair coat are also common. Many of these dogs develop a bloated appearance to their abdomen due to an increase of fat within the abdominal organs and a stretching of the abdominal wall as the organs get heavier. The pot-bellied appearance also develops because the muscles of the abdominal wall become weaker. Panting is another common finding with this disease.

How is it diagnosed?

A number of tests are necessary to diagnose and confirm Cushing's Disease. The primary one is the ACTH Stimulation Test. Other tests are needed to decide which form of the disease is present. Although some of these tests are somewhat expensive, they are necessary.

What are the treatment options?

- **Iatrogenic Cushing's Disease**

  Treatment of this form requires a discontinuation of the cortisone that is being given. This must be done in a very controlled manner so that other consequences do not occur. Unfortunately, it usually results in a recurrence of the disease that was being treated by the cortisone. Because there may have been adverse effects on the adrenal glands, treatment is also needed to correct that problem.

- **Adrenal Tumor**

  Treatment of an adrenal tumor requires major surgery. Although this surgery is dangerous to the dog, if it is successful and the tumor is not malignant, there is a good chance that the dog will regain normal health.

- **Pituitary Tumor**

  Treatment of the pituitary-induced form of Cushing's Disease is the most complicated. The drug, Lysodren™, is used to destroy the abnormal adrenal tissue. Lysodren™ is also known as mitotane. If not enough drug is used, the abnormal tissue persists and the disease continues. If too much is used, most or all of the adrenal cortex will be destroyed, which can be life-threatening. Therefore, careful monitoring of the dog is necessary in order to achieve good results. Because the pituitary is not being affected by the treatment, it continues to stimulate the adrenal gland. This means that continued treatment is necessary. Although a cure is not achieved, control is possible for many years if the tumor is small. If the tumor is large, local effects of the tumor invading surrounding tissues in the head can be the limiting factor in survival.

Be cautiously optimistic. This is a serious disease, but many dogs with Cushing's Disease enjoy a greatly improved quality of life for many years.

DEGENERATIVE DISK DISEASE

What is a disk, and what is its purpose?

The spinal cord is one of the most important and most sensitive organs in the body. If it is traumatized, its cells will not regenerate; injuries usually result in permanent damage. Therefore, the spinal cord is protected in a very special fashion. It goes through a bony canal within the spine; it is surrounded by protective bone everywhere except over the disks. This extreme protection reflects its importance and its fragility. Disks are rubber-like cushions between the vertebrae. They allow the back to move up and down and sideways without allowing contact between the bones of the spinal column.

What does it mean for a disk to rupture, and how does it happen?

The disk is composed of two parts. The outer covering is much like a thick shell. It is comprised of tough fibers that protect and contain the central part. It is thinnest at the top; this thin area is located just below the spinal cord. The central part of the disk has the consistency of thick toothpaste; it is much softer than the outer part.

When the outer shell degenerates, it allows the central part of the disk to escape. This is called a disk rupture or a ruptured disk. Since the shell is thinnest near the spinal cord, disk material that escapes almost always goes upward, putting pressure on the cord. Because the spinal cord is encased within its bony canal, it cannot move away from the pressure and it becomes pinched.

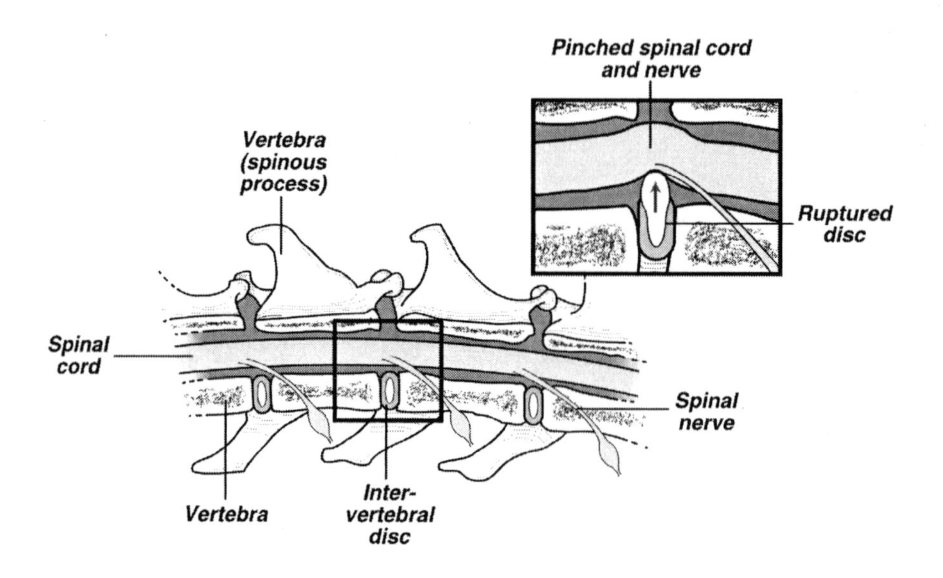

Diagram of longitudinal section through back-bone and inset showing rupture of degenerated disk causing pinching of spinal cord.

Degenerative disk disease causes spontaneous degeneration of the outer part of the disk, resulting in escape of the central part. It is not related to injury, although trauma can cause disks to rupture. It is also not related to age. Most dogs with degenerative disk disease are 3 - 7 years old. It is just a spontaneous event that is most likely controlled by genetic factors. Certain breeds, notably the Dachshund, Poodle, Pekinese, Lhaso Apso, and Cocker Spaniel have a high incidence of disk disease. Other breeds, such as the German Shepherd and Doberman Pinscher, also have disk disease but with a lower incidence. Many breeds never have degenerative disk disease.

Most owners report that a disk rupture occurred following some kind of traumatic event, such as a relatively small jump or fall. Although this act is frequently blamed for the disk rupture, if the disk had not already been degenerating, the rupture would not have occurred.

How does a ruptured disk affect the spinal cord?

The spinal cord is much like a telephone cable that is carrying thousands of tiny wires. When it is crushed, transmission of information through the wires is stopped. When the disk degenerates and ruptures, a similar event occurs. The central part is forced upward, putting pressure on the spinal cord and/or the nerves that leave the spinal cord over the disks (i.e., spinal nerves). Pressure on the spinal nerves results in pain; pressure on the spinal cord results in pain and/or loss of information transmission. This results in paralysis or partial paralysis.

Most disk ruptures occur in the middle to lower part of the back. However, they may also occur in the neck. The former often causes paralysis without severe pain; the latter often causes severe pain without paralysis. If paralysis affects all four legs, the disk rupture must be in the neck. Because of the way the nerve tracts are arranged in the spinal cord, disk ruptures in the neck may affect the rear legs first or even exclusively.

How fast do disks degenerate and rupture?

Disk degeneration usually occurs relatively slowly, i.e., over several days or weeks. The dog usually experiences pain and becomes reluctant to move. It may lie around for a few days allowing the body to resolve the problem, often without the owner being aware that a problem existed. However, disks may also rupture very acutely. Some dogs will go from normal walking to total paralysis in less than one hour.

How is a disk rupture diagnosed?

A presumptive diagnosis of disk disease is made based on the dog's history of neck or back pain, uncoordinated walking, or paralysis when there is no history of trauma. The physical examination will indicate that the problem originates from the spinal cord, giving further evidence to disk disease. Another important factor is the breed. If the dog is one of the high incidence breeds, the diagnosis is even more likely. In some cases, plain radiographs (x-rays) may assist the diagnosis, but they may also be normal since neither the disk nor the spinal cord are visible. If the diagnosis is in doubt or if surgery is to be performed, a myelogram may be done. This procedure involves injecting a special dye around the spinal cord while the dog is under anesthetic. When radiographs are taken, the dye will be seen outlining the spinal cord. A break in the dye column means that there is pressure on the spinal cord.

How do you know if the pressure on the spinal cord is due to a disk or something else?

It is possible that the pressure is due to a blood clot or a tumor. Both are possible but not very common, especially when compared to disk ruptures. If the breed of dog is correct for disk disease, there has been a sudden onset, and there has been no trauma, there is about a 95% chance that a disk rupture is causing the pressure. However, the diagnosis is not definite until the time of surgery.

Are all disk ruptures treated with surgery?

Not necessarily. Treatment is based on the stage of the disease. **Stage I** disk disease produces mild pain and is usually self-correcting in a few days. **Stage II** disk disease causes moderate to severe pain in the neck or lumbar (lower back) area. **Stage III** disk disease causes partial paralysis (paresis) and results in the dog walking in staggering or uncoordinated movements. **Stage IV** disk disease causes paralysis but the ability to feel is present. **Stage V** disk disease causes paralysis and loss of feeling. These stages tend to overlap in some dogs, and dogs may move from one stage to another over a period of hours to days.

Dogs with **Stage II and III** disease are usually treated with anti-inflammatory drugs, pain relievers, and restriction from exercise. Surgery may be considered if the pain or lack of coordinated movements persists after 4 - 7 days of treatment or if the neurological status declines from one day to the next. It is important that the dog not receive pain medication unless total confinement to a crate or cage is enforced. If the pain sensation is taken away, the dog is more likely to progress to total rupture of the disk. The sensation of pain is important for limiting motion. The length of confinement will vary among different dogs.

Dogs with **Stage IV** disease should have surgery, although a small percentage will recover without it. Dogs with **Stage V** disease should have surgery, and the sooner that surgery is done, the better the prognosis. If at all possible, these dogs should be operated on within the first 24 hours of the onset of paralysis.

What is the purpose of surgery?

The goal of surgery is to remove pressure from the spinal cord. If the disk rupture occurs in the lower back, a window is made in the side of the vertebral bone to expose the spinal cord. This window allows removal of disk material and relieves pressure from the cord. If the disk rupture occurs in the neck, a window is made in the bone exposing the spinal cord. This may be done either from the top or the bottom, depending on the situation and the training of the surgeon.

What is the success rate for treating disk disease with and without surgery?

Stage	*Recovery without Surgery*	*Recovery with Surgery*
II: up to 1 week	80-90%	90-95%
II: past 1 week	60-70%	90-95%
III	30-40%	85-95%
IV: up to 3 days	<25%	85-95%
IV: past 3 days	<20%	60-70%
V: up to 24 hours	<5%	50%
V: past 24 hours	<5%	<20%

When will we know if the surgery is successful?

When surgery is completed, we hope to achieve two things. First, the dog should be recovering from the anesthetic. Secondly, the disk rupture should be located and the pressure relieved from the spinal cord. However, the return of walking ability and relief from pain may not occur for several days, or even weeks, so success cannot be determined immediately.

When can my dog go home?

Following surgery, your dog will be hospitalized for 3 - 7 days. Bladder and bowel control are often lost when the dog is paralyzed, so it is best for control of these functions to return before going home. However, it is generally best not to extend hospitalization beyond 7 days because regaining the ability to walk partly depends on exercise and motivation. Since motivation is such an important part of the recovery process, visitation is encouraged beginning the day after surgery. Please ask about scheduling your visits.

If paralysis was present before surgery, your dog may not be able to walk when it is discharged from the hospital. You will be given detailed instructions on the procedures that should be performed. Recovery is dependent on four factors: whether or not permanent damage was done before surgery, if the surgery was performed promptly, physical therapy performed at home, and the motivation of your dog. You will be instructed on ways to achieve the last two.

Can my dog rupture a disk again?

The answer is "yes." However, more than 95% of degenerated disks will heal without surgery. So the chance of your dog needing surgery a second time is less than 5%.

What if the myelogram is normal?

The purpose of the myelogram is to identify pressure on the spinal cord. If the myelogram is normal, there is no pressure on the spinal cord. This has several important implications. First, it means that surgery will generally not be appropriate because the purpose of surgery is to relieve the pressure from the cord. Second, it means that one of the following conditions is likely to exist.

- **Spinal Shock**

  This is a temporary loss of spinal function that is generally associated with trauma. It occurs suddenly and is somewhat like a concussion of the brain. It may leave permanent damage, or full recovery may occur. Recovery from spinal shock generally occurs within a few hours to a few days.

- **Fibrocartilaginous Infarct or Embolism**

  In this condition, a small amount of disk material ruptures and gets into one of the blood vessels leading to the spinal cord. As the vessel narrows, the disk material obstructs it, depriving a certain segment of the spinal cord of its blood supply. Without proper blood supply, that segment of the spinal cord quits working, resulting in paralysis.

Surgery will not help these dogs because there is no pressure on the spinal cord. Often, paralysis involves only one rear leg, or one rear leg is more severely affected than the other. Complete recovery may occur in a few days to weeks, or there may be permanent damage to a portion of the spinal cord. Diagnosis of fibrocartilaginous infarct/embolism is based on the correct clinical signs and a normal myelogram. Confirmation requires a biopsy of the spinal cord so the diagnosis is confirmed only with an autopsy.

- **Degenerative Myelopathy**

This condition means that the spinal cord is slowly dying. It results in progressive paralysis that begins with the dog dragging its rear feet as it walks. This is called "knuckling over" and results in the toe nails of the rear feet being worn because they drag on the ground with each step. It progresses to weakness of the rear legs, then paralysis. It generally takes several weeks before paralysis occurs, and it generally occurs in large breeds of dogs, especially German Shepherds. Because there is no successful treatment and paralysis includes loss of urine and bowel control, euthanasia is generally recommended.

Diagnosis of degenerative myelopathy is based on the correct clinical signs, especially in large breeds of dogs, and a normal myelogram. Confirmation requires a biopsy of the spinal cord so the diagnosis is confirmed only with an autopsy.

A normal myelogram in a dog with slowly progressive paralysis is very frustrating because the two most likely diseases (numbers 2 and 3) cannot be confirmed without an autopsy.

DEMODECTIC MANGE

Mange is a parasitic skin disease caused by microscopic mites. Two different mange mites cause skin disease in dogs. One lives just under the surface of the skin, while the other resides in the hair follicles. Although both mites share some similar characteristics, there are also important differences. It is important not to confuse the two types of mange because they have different causes, treatments, and prognoses.

What causes demodectic mange?

Demodectic mange, sometimes just called "demodex", is the most common form of mange in dogs. It is caused by the demodectic mange mite, a parasite which lives in the hair follicles of affected dogs. Under the microscope, this mite appears shaped like an alligator with 8 legs. All dogs (and many humans) have a few of these mites on their skin. As long as the body's immune system is functioning, these mites cause no harm.

Demodectic mange most often occurs when a dog has an immature immune system, allowing the mites to grow rapidly. Therefore, this disease occurs primarily in dogs less than 12 - 18 months of age. In most cases, as a dog matures, the immune system also matures. Adult dogs which have the disease usually have defective immune systems.

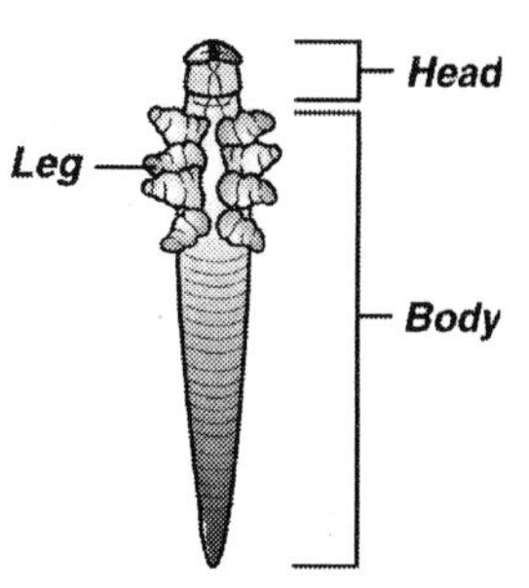

Demodex mite
(100x actual size)

Does this mean that demodectic mange is not contagious?

Yes. Since the mite is found on virtually all dogs, exposure of a normal dog to one with demodectic mange is not dangerous.

Why doesn't the immune system mature correctly in some dogs?

Development of the immune system is under genetic control. Thus, an affected dog usually comes from a litter containing other affected puppies. Owners of littermates should be put on the alert to watch for it. Because the disease is due to a genetic defect, affected dogs should not be bred. Also, parents of the affected dog should not be bred again.

What does demodectic mange do to the dog?

Surprisingly, a dog with demodectic mange does not itch severely, even though it loses hair in patches. Areas of bare skin will be seen. The hair loss usually begins on the face, especially around the eyes. When there are only a few patches of hair loss, it is termed **localized** demodectic mange. If the disease spreads to many areas of the skin, it becomes **generalized** demodectic mange.

How is demodectic mange treated?

The localized form is usually treated with topical medication. The generalized form requires shampoo therapy and a special dip or oral medication. Shampooing with special cleansing shampoos helps to flush out the hair follicles prior to dipping. Dipping is described below.

For dogs with generalized demodectic mange, secondary skin infections may represent a complicating factor requiring antibiotic therapy. Dogs with skin infections have very red, inflamed skin. This is the source of the term "red mange."

What is the prognosis for my dog?

Treatment of the localized form is generally successful. Treatment of the generalized form is also usually successful. However, if the immune system is defective, neither the mites nor the infection may respond to treatment.

Following successful treatment, is it likely to recur?

Because the immune system does not mature until 12 - 18 months of age, a dog with demodectic mange may have relapses until that age. It is important for re-treatment to begin promptly to minimize the possibility of developing uncontrollable problems. Demodectic mange may also occur in very old dogs because function of the immune system often declines with age. Dogs who have immune suppression due to illness or medication are also candidates for demodectic mange.

What kinds of dental problems do dogs have?

Dental disease is as common in dogs as it is in humans. The most common form of dental disease in humans is cavities. However, this is not the case in dogs. The most common form of canine dental disease is tartar buildup. This causes irritation of the gums around the base of the teeth (gingivitis), resulting in exposure of the roots. Ultimately, this leads to infection and tooth loss.

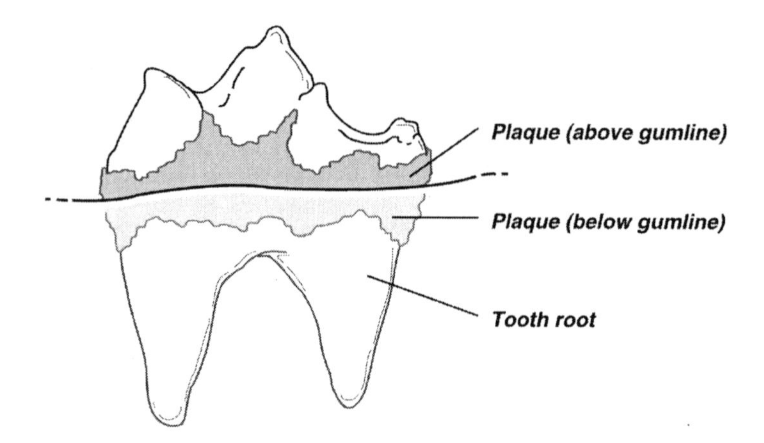

Molar Tooth with Dental Plaque

Isn't it correct that dogs that eat dry dog food don't have tartar buildup?

There are many misconceptions about tartar buildup in dogs. Diet is probably less important than most people think. Because dry food is not as sticky as canned food, it does not adhere to the teeth as much and thus, does not cause tartar buildup as rapidly. However, eating dry food does not remove tartar from the teeth. Once tartar forms, a professional cleaning is necessary. One of the main factors determining the amount of tartar buildup is the individual chemistry in the mouth. Some dogs need yearly cleanings; other dogs need a cleaning only once every few years.

What does tartar do to the teeth?

If tartar is allowed to remain on the teeth, several things may happen.

- The tartar will mechanically push the gums away from the roots of the teeth. This allows the teeth to loosen in their sockets and infection to enter the root socket. The teeth will loosen and fall out or have to be extracted.

- Infection will accumulate in the mouth, resulting in gingivitis, tonsillitis, and pharyngitis (sore throat).

- Although antibiotics may temporarily suppress the infection, if the tartar is not removed from the teeth, infection will return quickly.
- Infection within the mouth will be picked up by the blood stream and carried to other parts of the body.
- Some kidney and heart disease may be caused by this infection.

What is involved in cleaning my dog's teeth?

Proper cleaning of the teeth requires complete cooperation of the patient so plaque and tartar can be removed properly. Anesthesia is required to thoroughly clean the teeth. Although anesthesia always carries a degree of risk, the modern anesthetics in use in veterinary hospitals minimize this risk, even for older dogs. Depending on your dog's age and general health status, blood may be analyzed prior to anesthesia to evaluate blood cell counts and major organ function.

There are four steps in the cleaning process that will be used on your dog:

- ***Scaling*** removes the tartar above and below the gum line. This is done with hand instruments and ultrasonic cleaning equipment.
- ***Polishing*** smoothes the surface of the teeth, making them resistant to additional plaque formation.
- ***Flushing*** removes dislodged tartar from the teeth and helps to remove the bacteria that accompany tartar.
- ***Fluoride*** coating decreases teeth sensitivity, strengthens enamel, and decreases the rate of future plaque formation.

What type of scheduling is needed for teeth cleaning?

You should schedule the procedure with your veterinary clinic a few days in advance. It will be necessary to withhold food after 6 PM the night before; please do not remove the water. Your dog should be admitted to the hospital early and will generally be ready for discharge in the late afternoon. The dog will need to stay indoors that evening to insure that no accidents (falls, etc.) occur until complete recovery from anesthesia. If that is not possible, you may elect to have the dog spend the night in the hospital. The recovering dog should be offered small amounts of water and food that evening. By the next morning your dog will be completely recovered and you can feed and water normally.

What is diabetes mellitus?

There are two forms of diabetes in dogs: diabetes insipidus and diabetes mellitus. Diabetes insipidus is a very rare disorder that results in failure to regulate body water content. The more common type of diabetes is diabetes mellitus. This is a fairly common disorder and is most often seen in dogs 5 years of age or older. There is a congenital form that occurs in puppies, but this is not common. Diabetes mellitus is a disease of the pancreas. This is a small but vital organ that is located near the stomach. It has two significant populations of cells. One group of cells produces the enzymes necessary for proper digestion. The other group, called beta-cells, produces the hormone called insulin. Simply put, diabetes mellitus is a failure of the pancreas to regulate blood sugar.

Some people with diabetes take insulin shots, and others take oral medication. Is this true for dogs?

In humans, two types of diabetes mellitus have been discovered. Both types are similar in that there is a failure to regulate blood sugar, but the basic mechanisms of disease differ somewhat between the two groups.

- **Type I, or Insulin Dependent Diabetes Mellitus**, results from total or near-complete destruction of the beta-cells. This is the only type of diabetes known in dogs. As the name implies, dogs with this type of diabetes require insulin injections to stabilize blood sugar.
- **Type II, or Non-Insulin Dependent Diabetes Mellitus**, is different because some insulin-producing cells remain. However, the amount produced is insufficient, there is a delayed response in secreting it, and the tissues of the dogs body are relatively resistant to it. People with this form may be treated with an oral drug that stimulates the remaining functional cells to produce or release insulin in an adequate amount to normalize blood sugar. Because Type II diabetes does not occur in dogs, oral medications are not appropriate for treating diabetic dogs.

Why is insulin so important?

The role of insulin is much like that of a gatekeeper: it stands at the surface of body cells and opens the door, allowing glucose to leave the blood stream and pass inside the cells. Glucose is a vital substance that provides much of the energy needed for life, and it must work inside the cells. Without an adequate amount of insulin, glucose is unable to get into the cells. It accumulates in the blood, setting in motion a series of events which can ultimately prove fatal. When insulin is deficient, the cells become starved for a source of energy. In response to this, the body starts breaking down stores of fat and protein to use as alternative energy sources. As a consequence, the dog eats more; thus, we have weight loss in a dog with a ravenous appetite. The body tries to eliminate the excess glucose by excreting it in the urine. However, glucose (blood sugar) attracts water; thus, urine glucose takes with it large quantities of the body's fluids, resulting in the production of a large amount of urine. To avoid dehydration, the dog drinks more and more water. Thus, we have the four classical signs of diabetes:

- Weight loss
- Ravenous appetite
- Increased water consumption
- Increased urination

How is diabetes mellitus diagnosed?

The diagnosis of diabetes mellitus is based on three criteria: the four classical clinical signs, the presence of a persistently high level of glucose in the blood stream, and the presence of glucose in the urine. The normal level of glucose in the blood is 80 - 120 mg/dl (4.4 - 6.6 mmol/L). It may rise to 250 - 300 mg/dl (13.8 - 16.7 mmol/L) following a meal. However, diabetes is the only common disease that will cause the blood glucose level to rise above 400 mg/dl (22 mmol/L). Some diabetic dogs will have a glucose level as high as 800 mg/dl (44 mmol/L), although most will be in the range of 400 - 600 mg/dl (22 - 33 mmol/L). To keep the body from losing its needed glucose, the kidneys do not allow glucose to be filtered out of the blood stream unless very high levels of glucose are circulating in the blood. This means that dogs with a normal blood glucose level will not have glucose in the urine. Diabetic dogs, however, have excessive amounts of glucose in the blood, so it will be present in the urine.

What are the implications for me and my dog?

For the diabetic dog, one reality exists: blood glucose cannot be normalized without treatment. Although the dog can go a day or so without treatment and not get into a crisis, treatment should be looked upon as part of the dog's daily routine. Treatment almost always requires some dietary changes and administration of insulin. As for the owner, there are two implications: financial commitment and personal commitment. When your dog is well regulated, the maintenance costs are minimal. The special diet, insulin, and syringes are not expensive. However, the financial commitment is significant during the initial regulation process and if complications arise.

Initially, your dog will be hospitalized for a few days to deal with the immediate crisis and to begin the regulation process. The "immediate crisis" is only great if your dog is so sick that it has quit eating and drinking for several days. Dogs in this state, called ketoacidosis, may require a week or more of hospitalization with quite a bit of laboratory testing. Otherwise, the initial hospitalization may be only for a day or two to get some testing done and to begin treatment. At that point, your dog goes home for you to administer medication. At first, return visits are required every 3 - 7 days to monitor progress. It may take a month or more to achieve good regulation.

The financial commitment may again be significant if complications arise. Your veterinarian will work with you to try and achieve consistent regulation, but a few dogs are difficult to keep regulated. It is important that you pay close attention to instructions related to administration of medication, to diet, and to home monitoring. Another complication that can arise is hypoglycemia, or low blood sugar; if severe, it may be fatal. This may occur due to inconsistencies in treatment. Your personal commitment to treating this dog is very important in maintaining regulation and preventing crises. Most diabetic dogs require insulin injections once or twice daily. They must be fed the same food in the same amount on the same schedule every day. If you are out of town, your dog must receive proper treatment while you are gone. These factors should be considered carefully before deciding to treat a diabetic dog.

What is involved in treatment?

Consistency is vital to proper management of the diabetic dog. Your dog needs consistent administration of medication, consistent feeding, and a stable, stress-free lifestyle. To best achieve this, it is preferred that your dog live indoors. Although that is not essential, indoor living removes many uncontrollable variables that can disrupt regulation. The first step in treatment is to alter your dog's diet. Diets that are high in fiber are preferred because they are generally lower in sugar and slower to be digested. This means that the dog does not have to process a large amount of sugar at one time. The preferred diets are Prescription Diet Canine w/d™ and CNM OM™. If your dog is overweight, Prescription Diet Canine r/d™ is fed until the proper weight is achieved, then your dog is switched to one of the others.

Your dog's feeding routine is also important. The average dog prefers to eat about 10 - 15 times per day, one mouthful at a time. This means that food is left in the bowl at all times for free choice feeding. However, this is not the best way to feed a diabetic dog. The preferred way is to feed twice daily, just before each insulin injection. If your dog is currently eating on a free choice basis, please try to make the change. However, if your dog will not change or if you have several dogs that eat in a free choice fashion, you may find that this change is not practical. If a two-meals-per-day feeding routine will not work for you, it is still very important that you find some way to accurately measure the amount of food that is consumed.

The foundation for regulating blood glucose is the administration of insulin by injection. Many people are initially fearful of giving insulin injections. If this is your initial reaction, consider these points.

- Insulin does not cause pain when it is injected.
- The injections are made with very tiny needles that your dog hardly feels.
- The injections are given just under the skin in areas in which it is almost impossible to cause damage to any vital organ. Please do not decide whether to treat your dog with insulin until your veterinarian has demonstrated the injection technique. You will be pleasantly surprised at how easy it is.

Is continual or periodic monitoring needed?

It is necessary that your dog's progress be checked on a regular basis. Monitoring is a joint project on which owners and veterinarians must work together.

Home Monitoring

Your part consists of two forms of monitoring. First, you need to be constantly aware of your dog's appetite, weight, water consumption, and urine output. You should be feeding a constant amount of food each day which will allow you to be aware of days that your dog does not eat all of it or is unusually hungry after the feeding. You should weigh your dog at least once monthly. It is best to use the same scales each time. You should develop a way to measure water consumption. The average dog should drink no more than 7 1/2 oz. (225 mL) of water per 10 pounds (4.5 kg) of body weight per 24 hours. Since this is highly variable from one dog to another, keeping a record of your dog's water consumption for a few weeks will allow you to establish what is normal for your dog. Another way to measure water consumption is based on the number of times it drinks each day. When properly regulated, it should drink no more than six times per day. If this is exceeded, you should take steps to make an actual measurement. Any significant change in your dog's food intake, weight, water intake, or urine output is an indicator that the diabetes is not well controlled. You should consult your veterinarian for further blood testing.

The second method of home monitoring is to determine the presence of glucose in the urine. If your dog is properly regulated, there should be no glucose present in the urine. There are several ways to detect glucose in urine. You may purchase urine glucose test strips in any pharmacy. They are designed for use in humans with diabetes, but they will also work in the dog. A fresh urine sample should be collected and tested with the test strip. If glucose is detected, the test should be repeated for the next two days. If it is present each time, your veterinarian should see your dog for a blood test.

You should keep a small container to catch urine as the dog voids. A large amount of urine is not needed to test for urine glucose; it is not necessary to catch the entire amount of urine. Because the female dog usually squats to urinate, a shallow pan or dish may be placed under the hindquarters when she begins to urinate. For male dogs, urine can be collected as soon as the dog lifts the leg to void. Male dogs often urinate small amounts in several different places and most often urinate on vertical objects, such as bushes and trees.

Monitoring of Blood Glucose

Determining the level of glucose in the blood is the most accurate means of monitoring. This should be done about every 3 - 4 months if your dog seems to be well regulated. It should also be done at any time the clinical signs of diabetes are present or if glucose is detected in the urine for two consecutive days. Timing is important when the blood glucose is determined. Since eating will elevate the blood sugar for several hours, it is best to test the blood at least 6 hours after eating. When testing the blood we want to know the highest and lowest glucose readings for the day. The highest reading should occur just before an injection of insulin is given. The lowest should occur at the time of peak insulin effect. This is usually 5 - 8 hours after an insulin injection, but it should have been determined during the initial regulation process. Therefore, the proper procedure is as follows:

- Feed your dog its normal morning meal then take it to the hospital immediately. If you cannot get it to the hospital within 30 minutes, do not feed it. In that situation, bring its food with you.
- Take your dog to the hospital early in the morning without giving it insulin.
- If your dog gets excited or very nervous when riding in the car or being in the hospital, the glucose readings may be falsely elevated. If this occurs, it is best to admit your dog to the hospital the morning (or afternoon) before testing so it can settle down for testing the next day. Otherwise, the tests give limited information.

Does hypoglycemia (low blood sugar) occur in dogs?

Hypoglycemia means low blood sugar. If it is below 40 mg/dl (2.2 mmol/L), it can be life-threatening. Hypoglycemia occurs under two conditions:

- **If the insulin dose is too high.**

  Although most dogs will require the same dose of insulin for long periods of time, it is possible for the dog's insulin requirements to change. However, the most common causes for change are a reduction in food intake and an increase in exercise or activity. The reason for feeding before the insulin injection is so you can know when the appetite changes. If your dog does not eat, skip that dose of insulin. If only half of the food is eaten just give a half dose of insulin. Always remember that it is better for the blood sugar to be too high than too low.

- **If too much insulin is given.**

  This can occur because the insulin was not properly measured in the syringe or because two doses were given. You may forget that you gave it and repeat it, or two people in the family may each give a dose. A chart to record insulin administration will help to prevent the dog being treated twice.

The most likely time that a dog will become hypoglycemic is the time of peak insulin effect (5 - 8 hours after an insulin injection). When the blood glucose is only mildly low, the dog will be very tired and unresponsive. You may call it and get no response. Within a few hours, the blood glucose will rise, and your dog will return to normal. Since many dogs sleep a lot during the day, this important sign is easily missed. Watch for it; it is the first sign of impending problems. If you see it, please take your dog in for blood testing. If your dog is slow to recover from this period of lethargy, you should give it corn syrup (1 tablespoon by mouth). If there is no response in 15 minutes, repeat the corn syrup. If there is still no response, contact your veterinarian immediately for further instructions. If severe hypoglycemia occurs, a dog will have seizures or lose consciousness. This is an emergency that can only be reversed with intravenous administration of glucose. Call your veterinarian immediately.

DIARRHEA

What causes diarrhea?

Diarrhea is not a disease; rather, it is a symptom of many different diseases. Many mild cases of diarrhea can be resolved quickly with simple treatments. Others are the result of fatal illnesses, such as cancer. Even diarrhea caused by mild illnesses may become fatal if treatment is not begun early enough to prevent severe fluid and nutrient losses.

How serious is diarrhea in dogs?

We attempt to determine how sick the dog has become as a consequence of the diarrhea. When the dog is systemically ill (i.e., more than one body system is involved), some of the following may be noted:

- Vomiting
- Dehydration
- Loss of appetite
- Abdominal pain
- High fever
- Lethargy
- Bloody and/or watery diarrhea

What types of tests are performed to find the cause?

If diarrhea is associated with several of the above signs, a series of tests is performed in the hope that a diagnosis can be made. This permits more specific treatment. Diagnostic tests may include radiography (x-rays) with or without barium, blood tests, stool cultures, biopsies of the intestinal tract, and exploratory abdominal surgery. Once the diagnosis is known, treatment may include special medications and/or diets, or surgery.

If your dog does not appear systemically ill from diarrhea, the cause may be less serious. Some of the minor causes of diarrhea include stomach or intestinal viruses, intestinal parasites, and dietary indiscretions (such as eating garbage or other offensive or irritating materials). A minimum number of tests are performed to rule out certain parasites and infections. These cases may be treated with drugs to control the motility of the intestinal tract, drugs that relieve inflammation in the intestinal tract, and, often, a special diet for a few days. This approach allows the body's healing mechanisms to correct the problem. Expect improvement within 2 - 4 days; if this does not occur, a change in medication or further tests are done to better understand the problem. Please keep your veterinarian informed of lack of expected improvement so that the situation can be managed properly.

DIARRHEA QUESTIONNAIRE

Completing this questionnaire before consulting your veterinarian will greatly help in diagnosis.

- How long has the diarrhea been present?
- Is the diarrhea more severe now than a few days ago?
- Circle the word which applies to the diarrhea.

Consistency

Watery stool
Stool is the thickness of pancake batter

Blood

Very bloody stool
Only sporadic blood present
Blood not present in stool
Bright red blood present
Dark, tarry blood present

Degree/Frequency

Entire stool is soft or watery
Only portions of the stool are soft or watery
Diarrhea with each bowel movement
Diarrhea is sporadic (some bowel movements are normal)
Only 1 or 2 bowel movements per day
More than 4 bowel movements per day

Color

Stool is dark brown in color
Stool is very pale in color
Stool is black and tarry in appearance

Miscellaneous

Thick mucus or pieces of tissue present in stool
Loss of bowel control (defecates in the house on the floor)
Severe straining when having a bowel movement

- Is your dog's appetite normal?
- If not, is it eating at all?
- What have you been feeding your dog during the last week? (Include dog or cat foods, treats, table foods, milk, and anything else that it gets on a daily basis. Also state what percentage of the diet is each item or category.)
- Does your dog have access to foods other than what you feed it? If so, what?

- Has there been a significant diet change in the last few weeks?
- If so, does that correspond with the onset of the diarrhea?
- Is your dog as active as normal?
- Describe any change in water consumption (up or down).
- Has vomiting been occurring? If so, how frequently and for how long?
- Does your dog go outside your house?
- Does your dog go outside your yard?
- Does your dog have access to garbage cans, either within your house or yard or outside your yard?
- Does your dog have toys that it plays with that could have been swallowed?
- Does your dog have access to sewing materials, such as thread or needles, or rubber bands, or string?
- Do you have other dogs or cats that live with this one? If so, does the other pet have diarrhea?
- Do any of the members of your family currently have a diarrhea problem?

DILATED CARDIOMYOPATHY AND HEART FAILURE

Briefly, how does the heart work?

The heart has four chambers. The upper chambers are called atria (one chamber is called an atrium), and the lower chambers are called ventricles. In addition to the upper and lower chambers, the heart is also considered to have a right and a left side. Blood flows from the body into the right atrium. It is stored there briefly, then pumped into the right ventricle. The right ventricle pumps blood into the lungs, where it receives oxygen. It flows from the lungs into the left atrium; it is held here briefly before going into the left ventricle. The left ventricle contains the largest muscle of the heart so the blood can be pumped out to all parts of the body.

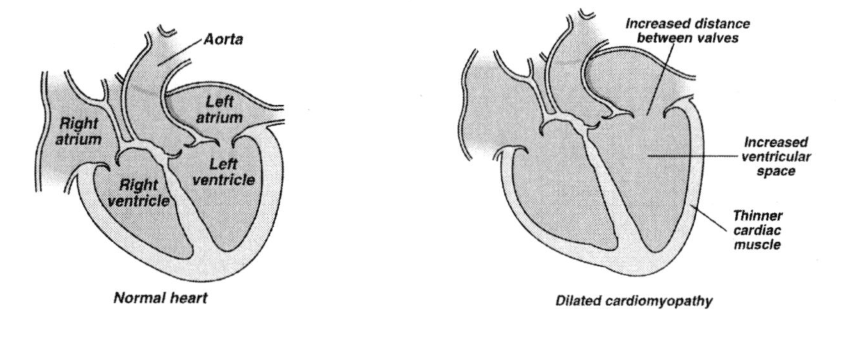

Normal heart

Dilated cardiomyopathy

What is dilated cardiomyopathy?

Dilated cardiomyopathy means that the heart muscle, especially the thick muscle wall of the left ventricle, becomes much thinner than normal. The pressure of the blood inside the heart then allows this thinned wall to stretch, resulting in a much larger left ventricular chamber. Therefore, the two characteristics of dilated cardiomyopathy are a heart wall that is much thinner than normal and a chamber that is much larger than normal.

How common is dilated cardiomyopathy?

Dilated cardiomyopathy is not the most common cause of heart failure in dogs in general. However, this is the most common cause of heart failure in *large breeds* of dogs. Small breeds are only occasionally affected. The most commonly affected breeds are Boxers, Doberman Pinschers, and Great Danes. Occasionally, medium sized breeds, notably Cocker Spaniels and English Springer Spaniels, are also affected.

Are there any signs of heart failure which would be noticeable to me?

When the heart is not properly pumping, blood backs up into the vessels of the lungs. Increased pressure within the vessels results in small amounts of fluid leaking out of the capillaries and eventually into the air passageways. This fluid collection in the lungs produces coughing and/or gagging, the most obvious sign of heart failure. Dogs in heart failure also tire very easily from minimal exercise.

Congestive heart failure begins when the heart is not able to provide blood with adequate oxygen to the tissues. Without adequate oxygen, the body's cells become desperate and trigger a series of responses. Various hormones are released by several organs in an attempt to correct the problem. These hormones conserve fluid in an effort to increase blood volume and the output of blood and oxygen by the heart. For several months, these compensatory responses help the situation. However, increased fluid retention eventually becomes harmful. More and more fluid leaks out of capillaries, causing increased gagging and coughing, and reduced stamina. Fluid may collect in the abdominal cavity and body tissues. Fluid in the lungs is called pulmonary edema, fluid below the skin is called peripheral or limb edema, and fluid in the abdomen is called ascites. Congestive heart failure is a common cause of these signs.

My dog seemed to get very ill just in the last day or two. How can this happen?

Dilated cardiomyopathy may have a very sudden onset. Some dogs go into severe heart failure in what appears to be a matter of hours. Rapid, heavy breathing, a blue tongue, excessive drooling, or collapse may be the first signs.

What tests are done to assess the situation?

There are several tests that are used. All provide valuable information while looking at different aspects of heart function.

- **Listening with a stethoscope (auscultation)**

  This valuable tool allows us to identify murmurs, their location, and their intensity and an abnormal heart rhythm (arrhythmia). It also allows us to hear lung sounds; this aids in our understanding of what is happening within the lungs.

- **Blood and urine tests**

  These do not give direct information about heart function, but they allow us to understand other disorders in the body that may impact on heart function and treatment of heart disease.

- **Chest radiographs (x-rays)**

  These give us the best look at the lungs and a view of the size and shape of the heart. In most cases, dilated cardiomyopathy causes tremendous enlargement of the heart. These changes are usually very apparent on the x-rays.

- **Electrocardiogram (ECG or EKG)**

  This is an assessment of the electrical activity of the heart. It allows us to accurately determine heart rate and to more accurately identify any arrhythmias which might be present.

- **Ultrasound examination (Sonogram, Echocardiogram)**

  This examination uses sound waves which bounce off the structures of the heart and are read on a TV-like monitor. It gives the most accurate determination of the size of each heart chamber, and permits measurement of the thickness of the heart walls. This is seen on the monitor in actual time so the contractions of the heart can be evaluated. Certain measurements can be taken which allow the actual strength of the heart's contraction to be measured as a number and compared to the normal animal. Ultrasound may not be available in all private veterinary practices because of the additional training needed to learn how to perform the examination and because of the cost of the equipment.

The combination of all of these tests gives us our best evaluation of the dog and its heart function. However, if cost considerations prohibit us performing all of them, two or three will provide much valuable information.

Is there a treatment for heart failure caused by dilated cardiomyopathy?

If the dog has a sudden onset of heart failure, rapid administration of the proper drugs is essential to survival. The following drugs may be used at various stages of treatment. Initial stabilization usually depends on the first two.

- ***Diuretics***

  These drugs stimulate the kidneys to remove excess fluid from the body. Furosemide is most commonly used, although others will be selected in certain circumstances.

- ***Nitroglycerin***

  This drug is called a venodilator; it dilates the veins throughout the body, especially the ones going to the heart muscle. It decreases the amount of blood returning to the heart by allowing some of it to "pool" in the veins. This takes some of the workload off the heart. This drug can be very useful for treating pulmonary edema, but it is only effective for a few days.

- ***Digitalis***

  This drug improves heart function in several ways. It regulates excess hormones that have been released, slows the heart rate, and strengthens each contraction of the heart.

- ***Enzyme blockers***

  This is a relatively new class of drugs which can directly block the compensation system that has gotten out of control.

- ***Vasodilators***

  These drugs dilate the arteries and/or the veins of the body so that the heart doesn't have to generate as much pressure to eject blood. They may be used long-term because they continue to be effective, as opposed to the short-term effects of nitroglycerin.

- ***Carnitine***

  A few dogs, especially Boxers, have a deficiency of this amino acid. This deficiency causes cardiomyopathy, and the administration of it will greatly improve heart function and even reverse the heart abnormalities. However, it is an expensive drug to give to large dogs, so it is not used unless its deficiency can be documented with blood tests.

How much longer will my dog live?

There are many factors that must be considered before that question can be answered. The results of the tests are important, and the response that occurs within the first few days is another indicator.

If response does not occur within a few hours to days, the prognosis is not good. However, most dogs that stabilize quickly will live for a period of a few months to many months, but the long-term prognosis is not good. It can be difficult to generate an accurate estimate for life-expectancy when a dog has heart disease because many variables impact on survival.

What is distemper?

Distemper is a highly contagious viral disease of domestic dogs, other members of the dog family, and some other species (for example ferrets, skunks and raccoons).

How is the disease spread?

The disease is spread mainly by direct contact of a susceptible dog with a dog showing symptoms. Coughing and sneezing can spread the virus over short distances.

What are the clinical signs?

As with all infectious diseases clinical signs can vary. The main signs are diarrhea, vomiting, thick, yellow discharge from eyes and nose, cough and later seizures. Dogs that recover from the disease are often left with persistent nervous muscle twitches (chorea) and recurrent seizures.

Are there other diseases causing similar signs?

There are many diseases which cause diarrhea and vomiting, several that cause the respiratory signs (cough, etc.), several that could cause neurological signs (seizures, etc.), but few which can cause all of these.

What is the treatment?

As with most viral infections there is no specific treatment. Antibiotics are ineffective against viruses. The treatment for distemper is aimed at helping reduce the signs and symptoms. This is accomplished with hospitalization providing rest and intensive nursing care, intravenous fluid therapy and symptomatic treatment for the vomiting, diarrhea, cough, etc.

How can I prevent my dog becoming infected?

Fortunately we have highly effective vaccines to use. These are given to pups along with other routine vaccines (*see* Vaccines and Vaccination p. 141). Although in the majority of dogs the protection from initial vaccination may last more than a year, annual revaccination is strongly recommended because, in some dogs the protection decreases more quickly. You cannot be certain that your dog is not one of those with less protection. Be sure to keep puppies away from dogs when you do not know if they are vaccinated and all dogs should be kept clear of wildlife.

How common is distemper?

It is a world-wide disease but fortunately because of successful vaccines it is much less common than it was before. It is still seen in populations where vaccination rates are low and in stray dogs. The virus may maintain in some recovered carrier dogs and wildlife such as skunks and raccoons. It is essential to keep vaccinating our dog population.

EAR (AURAL) HEMATOMA

What is a hematoma of the ear, and how does it occur?

An aural (ear) hematoma is a collection of blood, serum, or a blood clot within the pinna (ear flap). When present, the pinna will be very thick. The swelling may involve the entire pinna or it may involve only one area. When something irritates the ear canal, the dog responds by scratching or shaking the head. Excessive shaking causes blood vessels to break, resulting in bleeding. An understanding of the ear's anatomy makes the sequence of events more logical. The ear flap is composed of a layer of skin on each side of a layer of cartilage. The cartilage gives the ear flap its shape. Blood vessels go from side-to-side by passing through the cartilage. Violent shaking causes the vessels to break as the skin slides across the cartilage.

How is it treated?

There are four steps in treatment.

- **The blood is removed from the pinna.**

  This is accomplished by making a small incision in each end of the hematoma. A rubber drain tube is passed through the hematoma and sutured to the ear. This assures drainage of any more blood or serum that accumulates in the area.

- **The space where the blood accumulated is obliterated.**

  Since the skin over the hematoma has been pushed away from the cartilage, it must be reattached to it to prevent another hematoma from occurring. This is accomplished by a series of sutures that are passed through the ear flap.

- **The pinna is stabilized to prevent further damage.**

  The presence of the drain tube will cause the dog to shake its head even more. Shaking at this time may cause further damage to the pinna. Therefore, the pinna is laid on top of the dog's head and bandaged in place. Although the bandage may be somewhat cumbersome, it will prevent further damage to the pinna and allow proper healing to progress.

- **The cause of the problem is diagnosed and treated.**

  Another important aspect of treatment is dealing with the cause of the shaking. If an infection is present, medication is dispensed to treat it. However, some dogs have no infection but have foreign material (a tick, piece of grass, etc.) lodged in the ear canal. If so, the foreign material is removed. It is also possible that a foreign body initiated the shaking but was later dislodged. If that occurs, and no infection is present, further treatment of the ear canal is not needed.

Will I need to bring my dog back for further treatment?

The drain tube and bandage are generally removed in about 3 - 5 days. At that time, the hematoma is usually healed. There will be two holes in the skin where the drain tube entered. They will close within a few days. If discharge occurs from the holes before they close, it should be cleaned off with hydrogen peroxide. If an infection was present, it will be necessary to recheck the ear canal to be sure that the infection is gone. Otherwise, another hematoma may occur.

How common are ear infections in dogs?

Infection of the external ear canal (outer ear) by bacteria or yeast, is one of the most common types of infections seen in dogs. It is called otitis externa. Some breeds, such as Cocker Spaniels and Miniature Poodles, seem more prone to ear infections, but they may occur in any breed.

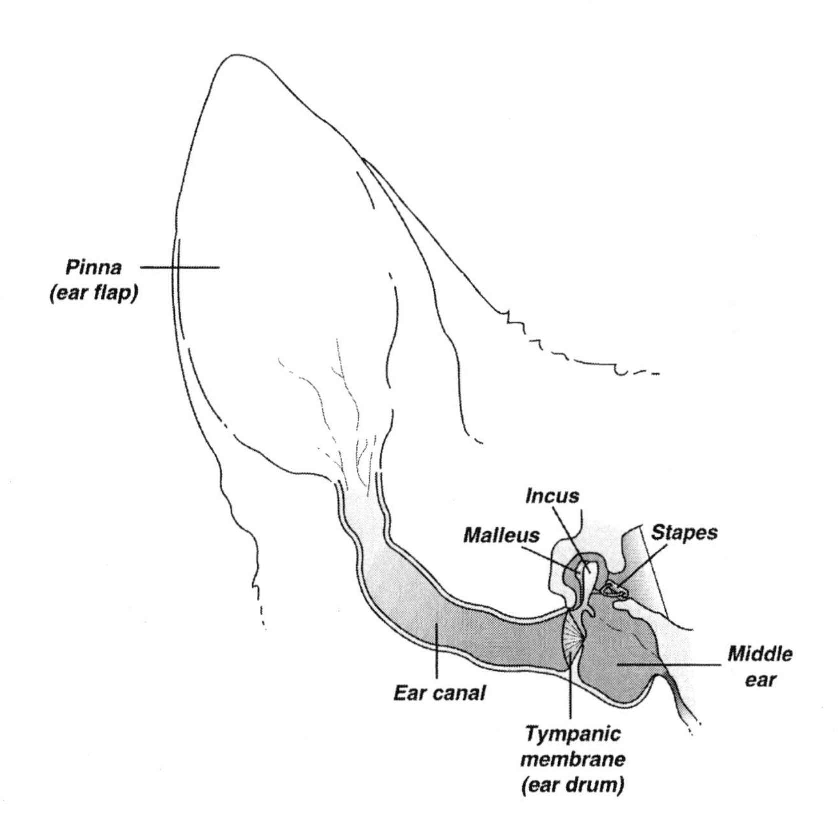

Diagrammatic section of ear showing external ear (pinna and vertical and horizontal canal) and middle ear (ear drum and ossicles: malleus, incus and stapes bones). The inner ear is not shown.

What are the symptoms of an ear infection?

A dog with an ear infection is uncomfortable and the ear canals are sensitive. The dog shakes its head and scratches its ears trying to get the debris and fluid out. The ears often become red and inflamed and develop an offensive odor. A black or yellowish discharge commonly occurs.

Don't these symptoms usually suggest ear mites?

Ear mites can cause several of these symptoms, including a black discharge, scratching, and head shaking. However, ear mite infections occur most commonly in puppies. Ear mites in adult dogs occur most frequently after a puppy carrying mites is introduced into the household. Sometimes, ear mites will create an environment within the ear canal which leads to a secondary infection with bacteria and yeast (fungus). By the time the dog is presented to the veterinarian, the mites may be gone, but a significant ear infection remains.

Since these symptoms are similar and usually mean an infection, can I just come by and get some medication?

There are several kinds of bacteria and at least one type of fungus which might cause an ear infection. Without knowing the kind of infection present, we do not know which drug to use. In some cases, the ear infection may be caused by a foreign body or tumor in the ear canal. Treatment with medication alone will not resolve these problems. Also, the dog must be examined to be sure that the eardrum is intact. Administration of certain medications can result in loss of hearing if the eardrum is ruptured. This determination is made by the veterinarian and must be done in the office.

How do you know which drug to use?

First, the ear canal is examined with an otoscope, an instrument that provides magnification and light. This permits a good view of the ear canal. This examination allows the determination of whether the eardrum is intact and if there is any foreign material in the canal. When a dog is in extreme pain and refuses to allow the examination, it may be necessary to sedate or completely anesthetize the dog for a thorough examination.

The next step is to examine a sample of the material from the ear canal to determine which organism is causing the infection. This is called cytology. Microscopic examination is very important in helping the veterinarian choose the right medication to treat the inflamed ear canal.

How are ear infections treated?

The results of the otoscopic examination and cytology usually determine the course of treatment. If there is a foreign body or tick lodged in the ear canal, the dog is sedated so that it can be removed. As stated previously, some dogs have such a heavy buildup of debris that sedation is needed to cleanse the canal and examine it completely. Cytologic study of debris from the ear canal dictates which drug to use. Sometimes, it reveals the presence of more than one type of infection (i.e., a bacterium and a fungus, or two kinds of bacteria); this situation usually requires the use of multiple medications or a broad-spectrum medication.

An important part of the evaluation of the patient is the identification of underlying disease. Many dogs with chronic or recurrent ear infections have allergies or low thyroid function (hypothyroidism). If underlying disease is suspected, it must be diagnosed and treated, if at all possible. If this cannot be done, the dog is less likely to have a favorable response to treatment. Also, the dog might respond temporarily, but the infection will recur (usually when ear medication is discontinued).

What is the prognosis?

Nearly all ear infections that are properly diagnosed and treated can be cured. However, if an underlying cause remains unidentified and untreated, the outcome will be less favorable. A progress check may be needed before the process is completed, but we expect ultimate success.

How important is it to treat an ear infection?

Dogs with ear infections are miserable. Their ears are a source of constant pain resulting in head shaking and scratching. However, that is not the only problem. Head shaking and scratching can also cause broken blood vessels in the ear flap, requiring surgery, and chronic ear infections can penetrate the ear drum and result in an internal ear infection.

My dog's ear canal is nearly closed. Is that a problem?

Closing of the ear canal is another result of a chronic ear infection. There are medications that can shrink the swollen tissues and open the canal in some dogs. However, some cases will eventually require surgery.

What is the goal of surgery?

The surgery for a closed ear canal is called a lateral ear resection. The goal of the surgery is to remove the vertical part of the ear canal and to remove swollen tissue from the horizontal canal. Removing the vertical canal should be successful, but removal of large amounts of tissue from the horizontal canal is more difficult. In some cases, the ear canal is surgically obliterated. This solves the canal problem, but it leaves the dog deaf on that side.

Is there anything I need to know about getting medication in the ear?

It is important to get the medication into the horizontal part of the ear canal. Be aware that the dog's external ear canal is "L" shaped. The vertical canal connects with the outside of the ear; the horizontal canal lies deeper in the canal and terminates at the eardrum. The ear canal may be medicated by following these steps:

- Gently pull the ear flap straight up and hold it with one hand.
- Apply a small amount of medication into the vertical part of the ear canal while continuing to keep the ear flap elevated. Hold this position long enough for the medication to run down to the turn between the vertical and horizontal canal.
- Put one finger in front of and at the base of the ear flap, and put your thumb behind and at the base.
- Massage the ear canal between your finger and thumb. A squishing sound tells you that the medication has gone into the horizontal canal.
- Release the ear and let your dog shake its head. If the medication contains a wax solvent, debris will be dissolved so it can be shaken out.
- If a second medication is to be used, apply it in the same manner.
- When all medications have been applied, clean the outer part of the ear canal and the inside of the ear flap with a cotton ball soaked with a small amount of rubbing (isopropyl) alcohol. Do not use cotton tipped applicators to do this as they tend to push debris back into the vertical ear canal.

What is canine ehrlichiosis?

Ehrlichiosis is an infectious disease of dogs. It first gained attention as a significant disease when military dogs returning from Vietnam during the 1970's were found to be infected. The disease seems to be particularly severe in German Shepherds and Doberman Pinchers.

The organism responsible for this disease is a rickettsial organism; rickettsiae are similar to bacteria. *Ehrlichia canis* is the most common species involved in ehrlichiosis, but occasionally, other strains of the organism will be found, i.e., *Ehrlichia platys*. Because of its origin in military dogs in Vietnam, it has also been called "tracker dog disease" and "tropical canine pancytopenia."

How does a dog get infected with ehrlichia?

Ehrlichiosis is transmitted to dogs through the bite of infected ticks; the brown dog tick, *Rhipicephalus sanguineus*, is the main reservoir of the organism in nature.

What are the signs of ehrlichiosis?

Signs of ehrlichiosis can be divided into three stages: acute (early disease), subclinical (no outward signs of disease), and chronic (long-standing infection). In areas where ehrlichiosis is common, many dogs are seen during the acute phase. Infected dogs may have fever, swollen lymph nodes, respiratory distress, weight loss, bleeding disorders, and, occasionally, neurologic disturbances. This stage may last 2 to 4 weeks.

The subclinical phase represents the stage of infection in which the organism is present but not causing any sign of disease. Sometimes, a dog will pass through the acute phase without its owner being aware of the infection. These dogs may become subclinical and develop laboratory changes yet have no apparent signs of illness. During this stage, the dog may eliminate the organism, or it may progress to the next stage.

This stage occurs because the immune system is not effective in eliminating or controlling the organism. Dogs are likely to develop a host of problems: anemia, thrombocytopenia (decreased platelets, the blood clotting cells), bleeding episodes, lameness, eye problems (including hemorrhage into the eyes), neurologic problems, and swollen limbs. If the bone marrow (site of blood cell production) fails, the dog becomes unable to manufacture any of the blood cells necessary to sustain life (red blood cells, white blood cells, and platelets).

How is ehrlichiosis diagnosed?

It may be difficult to diagnose infected dogs during the very early stages of infection. The immune system usually takes 2 - 3 weeks to respond to the presence of the organism and develop antibodies. Since the presence of antibodies to *Ehrlichia canis* is the basis of the most common diagnostic test, such dogs may be infected yet test negative. Testing performed a few weeks later will reveal the presence of antibodies and make confirmation of the diagnosis possible.

Rarely, the organism itself may be seen in blood smears or in aspirates of cells from lymph nodes, spleen, and lungs. This is a very uncommon finding. Therefore, detection of antibodies, coupled with appropriate clinical signs, is the primary diagnostic criteria.

How is ehrlichiosis treated?

Dogs experiencing severe anemia or bleeding problems may require a blood transfusion, initially. However, this does nothing to treat the underlying disease.

Drugs in the tetracycline family are the first choice to rid the dog of the organism that causes ehrlichiosis. Tetracycline hydrochloride and doxycycline are usually quite effective. Sometimes, chloramphenicol is used as a second choice for dogs unresponsive to tetracyclines, but it may have adverse effects on the bone marrow. Recently, evidence has been found that another antibiotic, enrofloxacin, may also be effective.

It has been traditionally recommended to treat infected dogs for 10 - 30 days, depending on the severity of the infection and clinical signs. Some of the newer research suggests that certain dogs may need to be treated for 2 - 4 months.

What is the prognosis?

Dogs with competent immune systems will usually recover, although they remain susceptible to reinfection. Dogs with weak immune systems and those which have progressed to the terminal stages of infection (bone marrow failure) have a guarded prognosis.

Can anything be done to prevent it?

Ridding the dog's environment of ticks is the most effective means of prevention. When this is not possible, low doses of one of the tetracyclines can be given during tick season.

Can I get ehrlichiosis from my dog?

No. However, humans can get canine ehrlichiosis. The disease is only transmitted to humans through the bites of ticks. Thus, although the disease is not transmitted directly from dogs to humans, infected dogs serve as sentinels to indicate the presence of infected ticks in the area and may be a source of the organism for infections in humans or other dogs.

What kinds of emergencies might occur?

There are many possible emergencies from road traffic accidents to acute internal problems such as an intestinal blockage, but the following are the most serious and require immediate attention.

- Any severe difficulty in breathing
- Cardiac failure
- Massive hemorrhage
- Profound shock from any cause
- Anaphylaxis (severe allergic reactions)
- Penetrating wounds of the thorax (chest) or abdomen
- Coma and loss of consciousness
- Poisoning
- Massive injuries to the body

What are some other emergencies where veterinary help must be sought at once?

Seizures, particularly if there is a loss of consciousness. Seizures may be due to epilepsy, head trauma, poisonings or occasionally other medical conditions.

- Eclampsia (milk fever) - see table
- Burns and scalds
- Heat stroke
- Hemorrhagic gastroenteritis (bloody diarrhea)
- Bites and fight wounds
- Severe bloat (gastric dilation) with or without twist (volvulus) - (*see* Bloat p. 9)
- Continuous vomiting and/or diarrhea

What can I do while getting veterinary help?

1) Keep calm.
2) Contact the veterinary hospital, tell them the situation and get first aid advice.
3) Keep the animal warm, as quiet as possible, and keep movement to a minimum if there is possible trauma - broken limbs, etc.
4) For specific aid refer to the following table.
5) Obtain a suitable container such as a strong cardboard box. Drop a blanket or thick towel over the patient. Tuck in carefully or maneuver animal onto blanket to lift gently into transport container or directly into car.
6) Get to the veterinary hospital as soon as possible, but drive carefully.

Caution: Dogs who are in severe pain or frightened may bite their owners!

Emergency Situation	*Action*
Road traffic accident	Make sure animal has clear airway (do not put hand in mouth), keep warm with blanket (also helps restrain if frightened or aggressive). Cover wounds with cleanest material available. Handle with care, supporting body as much as possible and carry in basket, box or cage to veterinary hospital.
Bleeding (hemorrhage)	If severe hemorrhage from cut or open wound apply tourniquet just tight enough to significantly reduce flow of blood; has to be loosened within 20 minutes. Apply pad of cotton wool over gauze dressing to wound or bleeding point and bandage firmly and/or apply pressure.
Seizures	Avoid animal injuring itself. Do not put hand in mouth, use handle or similar to prevent teeth clamping tongue. Keep animal as quiet as possible and in low light.
Burns and scalds	Cool the burned area with cool water, for example running water or soaked towels. This also helps remove caustic substances (acid or alkaline) if these are the cause. If loss of skin, cover with cleanest material available.
Eclampsia (milk-fever) (usually seen in bitches 1 to 3 weeks after whelping: excessive panting, wild eyes, muscle spasms and weakness, maybe seizures)	Remove from puppies, call vet immediately. Easily treated but can be rapidly fatal.
Heat stroke (animals left in a car in summer with little or no ventilation; excessive panting and obvious distress)	Cool with water.
Hemorrhagic gastroenteritis (diarrhea with blood; with or without vomiting)	Seek veterinary attention.
Bites, fight wounds	Clean with soapy water. Require veterinary attention and antibiotics.

Mismating/unwanted mating	If dogs are still together ('tied'), do not try to pull apart. Seek veterinary attention within 8 - 24 hours.
Poisons	Induce vomiting with 5 mL (teaspoon) of hydrogen peroxide orally or a teaspoon of salt placed in the mouth. Keep sample of vomit. DO NOT INDUCE VOMITING if animal has ingested corrosive material such as strong acid, alkali, or petroleum-based products. If corrosive or toxic material on skin, wash profusely. Bring sample of suspected poison with container to the veterinary hospital.
Eye damage	If cornea penetrated or perforated it will be very painful. Prevent animal scratching at eye and doing further damage. If eyeball out of socket (proptosis) keep moist with saline solution (eg contact lens solution) and protect with soft, clean material soaked in saline.
Shock (*see below*)	Keep the animal warm and quiet. Seek immediate veterinary help.

What is shock?

Shock has many definitions. It is a complex body reaction to a number of situations. These include acute loss of blood volume such as in hemorrhage, heart failure and other causes of decreased circulation (e.g. severe and sudden allergic reaction and heat stroke). If not treated quickly and effectively shock may cause irreversible injury to body cells, and it can be rapidly fatal.

How do I recognize shock?

Signs include rapid breathing which may be noisy, rapid heart rate with a weak pulse, pale (possibly even white) mucus membranes (for instance gums, lips, under eyelids) and severe depression (listlessness) and cool extremities (limbs and ears).

What should I do?

Seek veterinary help immediately. Keep the dog warm and quiet.

What should I do to kill the fleas on my dog?

This is a simple question with a rather complex answer. Successful flea control has two aspects. Fleas must be controlled on your dog, and fleas must be controlled in your dog's environment. Since dogs and cats share the same fleas, the presence of a cat in your dog's environment makes flea control much more difficult. To appreciate the complex issue of flea control, you must understand something about the flea's life cycle.

Fleas seem to be rather simple. How complicated can their life cycle be?

Although you are only able to see the adult flea, there are actually 4 stages of the life cycle. The adult flea constitutes only about 5% of the entire flea population if you consider all four stages of the life cycle. Flea eggs are pearly white and about 1/32" (1/2 mm) in length. They are too small to see without magnification. Fleas lay their eggs on the dog, but the eggs do not stick to the dog's hair. Instead, they fall off into the dog's environment. The eggs make up 50% of the flea population. They hatch into larvae in 1 to 10 days, depending on temperature and humidity. High humidity and temperature favor rapid hatching.

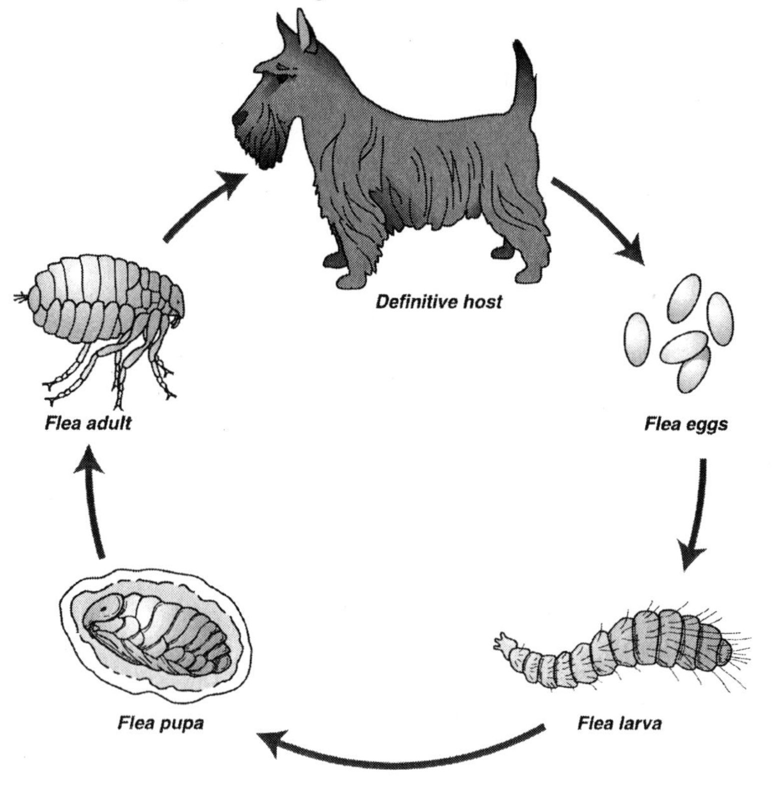

LIFE CYCLE OF DOG FLEA

Flea larvae are slender and about 1/8 - 1/4" (2 to 5 mm) in length. They feed on organic debris found in their environment and on adult flea feces, which is essential for successful development. They avoid direct sunlight and actively move deep into carpet fibers or under organic debris (grass, branches, leaves, or soil). They live for 5 to 11 days before becoming a pupa.

Moisture is essential for the survival of these immature stages of the flea; larvae are killed by drying. Therefore, it is unlikely that they survive outdoors in shade-free areas. Outdoor larval development occurs only where the ground is shaded and moist and where flea-infested pets spend a significant amount of time. This allows flea feces to be deposited in the environment. In an indoor environment, larvae survive best in the protected environment of carpet or in cracks between hardwood floors. They thrive in humid climates.

Following complete development, the mature larvae produce a silk-like cocoon in which the next step of development, the pupa, resides. The cocoon is sticky, so it quickly becomes coated with debris from the environment. This serves to camouflage it. In warm, humid conditions, pupae become adult fleas in 5 - 10 days. However, the adults do not emerge from the cocoon unless stimulated by physical pressure, carbon dioxide, or heat.

Pre-emerged adult fleas can survive up to 140 days within the cocoon. During this time, they are resistant to insecticides applied to their environment. Because of this, adult fleas may continue to emerge into the environment for up to 3 weeks following insecticide application. When the adult flea emerges from its cocoon, it immediately seeks a host because it must have a blood meal within a few days to survive. It is attracted to people and pets by body heat, movement, and exhaled carbon dioxide. It seeks light, which means that it migrates to the surface of the carpet so that it can encounter a passing host. Following the first blood meal, female fleas begin egg production within 36 to 48 hours. Egg production can continue for as long as 100 days, which means that a single flea can produce thousands of eggs.

This entire life cycle (adult flea —> egg —> larva—> pupa —> adult) can be completed in 14 - 21 days with the proper temperature and humidity conditions. This adds to the problem of flea control.

What can these fleas do to my dog?

If untreated, the female flea will continue to take blood for several weeks. During that time, she will consume about 15 times her body weight in blood. Although the male fleas do not take as much blood, they, too, contribute to significant blood loss. This can lead to the dog having an insufficient number of red blood cells, which is known as anemia. In young or debilitated dogs, the anemia may be severe enough to cause death. Contrary to popular belief, most dogs have rather limited itching due to flea bites. However, many dogs become allergic to the saliva in the flea's mouth. When these dogs are bitten, intense itching occurs, causing the dog to scratch and chew on its skin (*see* 'Flea Allergy' p. 67).

What can I do to rid my dog of fleas?

Successful flea control must rid the dog of fleas and it must rid the dog's environment of fleas. In fact, environmental control is probably more important than what is done to the dog. If your dog remains indoors and you do not have other pets that come in from the outside, environmental control is relatively easy. However, the dog that goes outdoors or stays outdoors presents a significant challenge. It may be impossible to completely rid the environment of fleas under these conditions, though flea control should still be attempted. When the dog is free-roaming or other dogs are allowed access to the dog's yard, the task of flea control becomes even more difficult.

What can I do to my dog?

Many insecticides that are applied to the dog have limited effectiveness against fleas because they are only effective for a few hours after application. Also, most of these products are effective only against adult fleas. Flea powders, sprays, and shampoos will kill the fleas present on your dog at the time of application. However, most of these products have little or no residual effects, so the fleas that return to your dog from his environment are not affected. Thus, your dog may be covered with fleas within a day after having a flea bath or being sprayed or powdered.

There are some newer, more effective sprays that can be a valuable part of the overall treatment plan. They kill adult fleas rapidly and are safe enough to use daily, if necessary. Flea sprays containing insect growth regulators are helpful in managing the overall problem because they help to break the flea life cycle. Some of the newer pet sprays with growth regulators are not recommended for daily use; once weekly application is recommended. Always read the label when using any new product on a dog.

Currently, some other types of products are available which have residual effects (i.e., that last for several days). These are flea collars and flea dips. Flea dip is poured over your dog after it has been bathed. The dip is not rinsed off and is allowed to dry on the skin and hair. This results in residual flea control for 4 - 5 days, but not for several weeks as some people think. Flea collars are on the dog and working 24 hours per day. However, they are not very effective in climates that are especially conducive to flea reproduction. Also, some dogs develop irritated skin in response to the collars; obviously, these dogs should not wear collars.

What can I do to my dog's environment?

Environmental flea control usually must be directed at your house and your yard. Even though fleas may be in your house, most people never see them. Fleas greatly prefer dogs and cats to people; they only infest humans when there has not been a dog or cat in the house for several days. (There are exceptions to this.) A professional exterminator may be called to treat your house or you may use a house fogger or a long-lasting spray. These foggers and sprays are very effective for adult fleas, but they will not kill adults that are still in their cocoon. You should purchase a fogger or a spray that kills the adult fleas and inhibits development of the eggs and larvae. In climates with extended warm temperatures and high humidity, it may be necessary to treat two or three times with a 30-day residual product before all stages of the fleas are removed from the house. The second treatment is most effective if it is done 2 weeks after the first.

Yard control may also be done by a professional exterminator or with various insecticides you may use yourself. Be sure that any insecticide used has a 30-day residual. This keeps you from having to spray every week. In climates with extended warm temperatures and high humidity, it will often be necessary to treat monthly during the warm months of the year. You should use a 30-day residual product each time. Some of the newest products which contain the growth regulator fenoxycarb are labeled for use only once or twice a year. Your veterinarian is able to help you choose the most effective product for your situation.

I have heard of a treatment for the house guaranteed for 1 year. Is that true?

There is at least one company that will treat your carpet with a flea-killing powder. The powder is non-toxic to people. It is worked deeply into the carpet to prevent it from being removed by vacuuming. This treatment has proven very successful, even in the face of heavy flea infestations. However, the treatment does not address fleas in your yard. The same chemical, a form of boric acid, is also available for application by the home owner. However, the self application kits do not offer the year guarantee.

Another option is a treatment which contains the insect growth regulator, fenoxycarb. As stated previously, these products are recommended for use once or twice a year. Fenoxycarb has no activity against adult fleas but is very helpful in inhibiting the development of eggs and larvae. It is a hormone-like substance which works against the juvenile stages of the flea; it is not an insecticide and is a safe choice when children are in the home.

What about the once a month flea products that are now available?

These products have many advantages over the products that have been used in the past. The monthly tablet is effective, but it does not have any effect on adult fleas. Rather, it causes the female fleas to lay abnormal eggs that do not hatch. To kill the adult fleas, you must use the other products that have been mentioned. The topical products kill adult fleas, usually before they have a chance to bite your dog. They are applied in one or two locations and spread over the body. There is no odor or skin irritation. They are quite resistant to being washed off so they remain effective even after swimming or bathing. For dogs in environments that permit continual exposure to new fleas, the topical products are usually the most effective approach.

I have not seen fleas on my dog. Does that mean that none are present?

When a dog is heavily infested with fleas, it is easy to find them. If the numbers are small, it is best to quickly turn your dog over and look on its belly. If you do not find them there, look on the back just in front of the tail. Be sure to part the hair and look at the level of the skin. When the numbers are very small, look for "flea dirt." Flea dirt is fecal matter from the flea that contains digested blood. Finding flea dirt is a sure indication that fleas are present or have been present recently.

Flea dirt looks like pepper. It varies from tiny black dots to tubular structures about 1/32" (1/2 mm) long. If you are in doubt of its identification, put the suspected material on a light colored table top or counter top. Add one or two drops of water, and wait about 30 seconds. If it is flea dirt, the water will turn reddish brown as the blood residue goes into solution. Another method is to put some of the material on a white paper towel and then wet the paper towel with water. A red stain will become apparent if you gently wipe the material across the surface of the paper towel.

Many people find tiny drops of blood in a dog's bedding or where the dog sleeps. This is usually flea dirt that was moistened, then dried. It leaves a reddish stain on the bedding material and is another sign that fleas are present.

I just got my dog home from boarding and it has fleas. Doesn't that mean that it got them at the boarding facility?

Not necessarily. If you recall, pre-emerged adult fleas can survive up to 140 days within the cocoon. This is significant when your pets are gone from home for extended periods of time. During the time that the house is quiet and empty, pre-emerged adults remain in their cocoon. Even if the house was treated with an insecticide, their cocoon protects them. When people and pets return to the house, adults emerge from their cocoons and immediately begin to seek a blood meal. They jump on dogs, cats, and even people. Although it may appear that a dog just returned from boarding brought fleas to your home, it is also very possible that a sudden emergence of adult fleas may account for the fleas present.

FLEA ALLERGY

What are allergies, and how do they affect dogs?

One of the most common conditions affecting dogs is allergy. In the allergic state, the dog's immune system "overreacts" to foreign substances (allergens or antigens) to which it is exposed. These overreactions are manifested in three ways. The most common is itching of the skin, either localized (one area) or generalized (all over the dog). Another manifestation involves the respiratory system and may result in coughing, sneezing, and/or wheezing. Sometimes, there may be an associated nasal or ocular (eye) discharge. The third manifestation involves the digestive system, resulting in vomiting or diarrhea. The specific response that occurs is related to the type of allergy present.

Does that mean that there are several types of allergies?

There are five known types of allergies in the dog: contact, flea, food, bacterial, and inhalant. Each of these has some common expressions in dogs, and each has some unique features.

What is meant by the term flea allergy?

In spite of common belief, a normal dog experiences only minor skin irritation in response to flea bites. Even in the presence of dozens of fleas, there will be very little itching. On the other hand, the flea allergic dog has a severe, itch-producing reaction to flea bites. This occurs because the dog develops an allergic response to the flea's saliva. When the dog is bitten, flea saliva is deposited in the skin. Just one bite causes intense itching.

What does this reaction do to the dog?

The dog's response to the intense itching is to chew, lick, or scratch. This causes hair loss and can lead to open sores or scabs on the skin, allowing a secondary bacterial infection to begin. The area most commonly involved is over the rump (just in front of the tail). This is probably because fleas find this part of the dog more desirable. Many flea-allergic dogs also chew or lick the hair off of their legs.

What is the proper treatment?

The most important treatment for flea allergy is to get the dog away from all fleas. Therefore, strict flea control is the backbone of successful treatment (*see* 'Fleas' p. 63). There are many products available for flea control, and many work in entirely different manners. In some cases, multiple products may be needed. Some are used on the dog and some in the dog's environment. Unfortunately, complete flea control is not always possible for dogs that live outdoors in warm and humid climates, where a new population of fleas can hatch out every 14 - 21 days. Some dogs can be desensitized to the adverse effects of flea bites. Flea saliva extract (flea antigen) is injected into the dog in tiny amounts over a prolonged period of time. This is an attempt to reprogram the dog's immune system so it no longer over-reacts to flea bites. If successful, itching no long occurs or is less intense when the dog is bitten. However, this approach is only successful about 50 - 75% of the time. When strict flea control is not possible, corticosteroids (or "cortisone" or "steroids") can be used to block the allergic reaction and give relief. This is often a necessary part of dealing with a flea allergy. Some dogs respond best to long-acting injections and others to oral medication. Dogs are more resistant to the side-effects of steroids than humans, but significant side-effects can occur. For this reason, the goal is to administer the smallest amount of steroid needed to keep the dog comfortable. Some dogs develop a secondary bacterial infection in the skin. When this occurs, appropriate antibiotics must be used.

FOOD ALLERGY

What are allergies, and how do they affect dogs?

One of the most common conditions affecting dogs is allergy. In the allergic state, the dog's immune system "overreacts" to foreign substances (allergens or antigens) to which it is exposed. These overreactions are manifested in three ways. The most common is itching of the skin, either localized (one area) or generalized (all over the dog). Another manifestation involves the respiratory system and may result in coughing, sneezing, and/or wheezing. Sometimes, there may be an associated nasal or ocular (eye) discharge. The third manifestation involves the digestive system, resulting in vomiting or diarrhea.

Are there several types of allergies?

There are five known types of allergies in the dog: contact, flea, food, bacterial, and inhalant. Each of these has some common expressions in dogs, and each has some unique features.

What is food allergy?

A food allergy is a condition in which the body's immune system reacts adversely to a food or an ingredient in a food.

What foods are likely to cause an allergic reaction?

Any food or food ingredient can cause an allergy. However, protein, usually from the meat source of the food, is the most likely offender. Proteins commonly found in dog foods are derived from beef, chicken, lamb, and horsemeat.

Isn't a lamb-based dog food supposed to be hypoallergenic?

No, although many people think it is. Several years ago there were no dog foods on the commercial market that contained lamb. A manufacturer of prescription dog foods formulated a food from lamb that was suitable for allergy testing, which will be explained below. Because of that situation, lamb-based dog food was considered "hypoallergenic." Dogs are not likely to be born with food allergies. More commonly, they develop allergies to food products they have eaten for a long time. The allergy most frequently develops in response to the protein component of the food; for example, beef, pork, chicken, or turkey. Food allergy may produce any of the clinical signs previously discussed, including itching, digestive disorders, and respiratory distress. Testing for food allergy is recommended when the clinical signs have been present for several months, when the dog has a poor response to steroids, or when a very young dog itches without other apparent causes of allergy. Testing is done with a special hypoallergenic diet. Because it takes at least 4 weeks for all other food products to get out of the system, the dog must eat the special diet exclusively for 4 - 8 weeks (or more). If positive response occurs, you will be instructed on how to proceed. *If the diet is not fed exclusively, it will not be a meaningful test.* This cannot be overemphasized. If any type of table food, treats or vitamins are given, it must be discontinued during the testing period. There may be problems with certain types of chewable heartworm preventative, as well. Your veterinarian will discuss this with you. Because dogs that are being tested for inhalant allergy generally itch year round, a food allergy dietary test can be performed while the inhalant test and antigen preparation are occurring.

What are Giardia?

Giardia are sometimes confused with worms because they invade the gastrointestinal tract and can cause diarrhea. They are not worms; instead, they are one-celled parasites classified as protozoa.

Most dogs that are infected with *Giardia* do not have diarrhea or any other signs of illness. When the eggs (cysts) are found in the stool of a dog without diarrhea, they are generally considered a transient, insignificant finding. However, in puppies and debilitated adult dogs, they may cause severe, watery diarrhea that may be fatal.

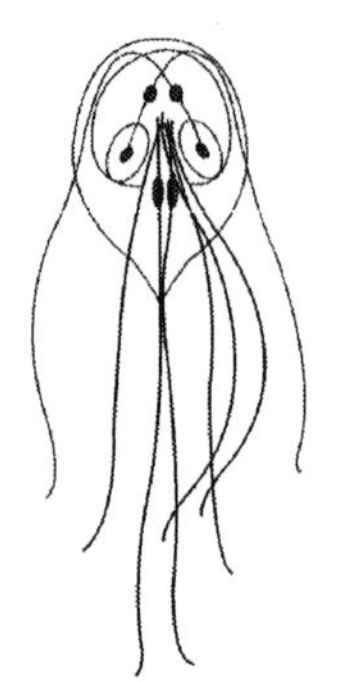

Giardia: 750 x actual size (after Kofold and Christiansen)

How did my dog get Giardia?

A dog becomes infected with *Giardia* when it swallows the cyst stage of the parasite. Once inside the dog's intestine, the cyst goes through several stages of maturation. Eventually, the dog is able to pass infective cysts in the stool. These cysts lie in the environment and can infect other dogs. They may also be transmitted through drinking *infected* water.

How is giardiasis diagnosed?

Giardiasis is diagnosed by performing a microscopic examination of a stool sample. The cysts are quite small and usually require a special floatation medium for detection, so they are not normally found on routine fecal examinations. Occasionally, the parasites may be seen on a direct smear of the feces. A blood test is also available for detection of antigens (cell proteins) of *Giardia* in the blood. This test is probably more accurate than the stool exam, but it requires several days to get a result from the laboratory performing the test.

How is giardiasis treated?

The typical drug used to kill *Giardia* is metronidazole, an antibiotic-type drug. It is given for 5 - 7 days. Other drugs are also used if diarrhea and dehydration occur. If metronidazole is not effective, others are available.

Can humans become infected with Giardia?

Giardia can also cause diarrhea in humans and children are especially susceptible. Therefore, environmental disinfection is important. The use of chlorine bleach, one cup in a gallon (500 mL in 4 liters) of water, is effective if the surfaces and premises can be safely treated with it.

GRIEF MANAGEMENT IN CHILDREN

The death of a cherished pet creates a sense of loss for adults and produces a predictable chain of emotions. The stages of grief are typically denial, sadness, depression, guilt, anger, and, finally, relief (or recovery). However, the effects on children vary widely depending upon the child's age and maturity level. The basis for their reaction is their ability to understand death.

Two and Three Year Olds

Children who are two or three years old typically have no understanding of death. They often consider it a form of sleep. They should be told that their pet has died and will not return. Common reactions to this include temporary loss of speech and generalized distress. The two or three year old should be reassured that the pet's failure to return is unrelated to anything the child may have said or done. Typically, a child in this age range will readily accept another pet in place of the dead one.

Four, Five, and Six Year Olds

Children in this age range have some understanding of death but in a way that relates to a continued existence. The pet may be considered to be living underground while continuing to eat, breathe, and play. Alternatively, it may be considered asleep. A return to life may be expected if the child views death as temporary. These children often feel that any anger they had for the pet may be responsible for its death. This view should be refuted because they may also translate this belief to the death of family members in the past. Some children also see death as contagious and begin to fear that their own death (or that of others) is imminent. They should be reassured that their death is not likely. Manifestations of grief often take the form of disturbances in bladder and bowel control, eating, and sleeping. This is best managed by parent-child discussions that allow the child to express feelings and concerns. Several brief discussions are generally more productive than one or two prolonged sessions.

Seven, Eight, and Nine Year Olds

The irreversibility of death becomes real to these children. They usually do not personalize death, thinking it cannot happen to themselves. However, some children may develop concerns about death of their parents. They may become very curious about death and its implications. Parents should be ready to respond frankly and honestly to questions that may arise. Several manifestations of grief may occur in these children, including the development of school problems, learning problems, anti-social behavior, hypochondriacal concerns, or aggression. Additionally, withdrawal, over attentiveness, or clinging behavior may be seen. Based on grief reactions to loss of parents or siblings, it is likely that the symptoms may not occur immediately but several weeks or months later.

Ten and Eleven Year Olds

Children in this age range generally understand death as natural, inevitable, and universal. Consequently, these children often react to death in a manner very similar to adults.

Adolescents

Although this age group also reacts similarly to adults, many adolescents may exhibit various forms of denial. This usually takes the form of a lack of emotional display. Consequently, these young people may be experiencing sincere grief without any outward manifestations.

HEARTWORM DISEASE

What causes heartworm disease?

Heartworm disease (dirofilariasis) is a serious and potentially fatal disease in dogs. It is caused by a worm called *Dirofilaria immitis*. Heartworms are found in the heart and large adjacent vessels of infected dogs. The female worm is 6 to 14 inches (15 to 35 cm) long and 1/8 inch (5 mm) wide; the male is about half the size of the female. One dog may have as many as 300 worms.

How do heartworms get into the heart?

Adult heartworms live in the heart and pulmonary arteries of infected dogs. They have been found in other areas of the body, but this is unusual. They survive up to 5 years and, during this time, the female produces millions of young (microfilaria). These microfilaria live in the bloodstream, mainly in the small blood vessels. The immature heartworms cannot complete the entire life cycle in the dog; the mosquito is required for some stages of the heartworm life cycle. The microfilaria are therefore not infective (cannot grow to adulthood) in the dog, although they do cause problems.

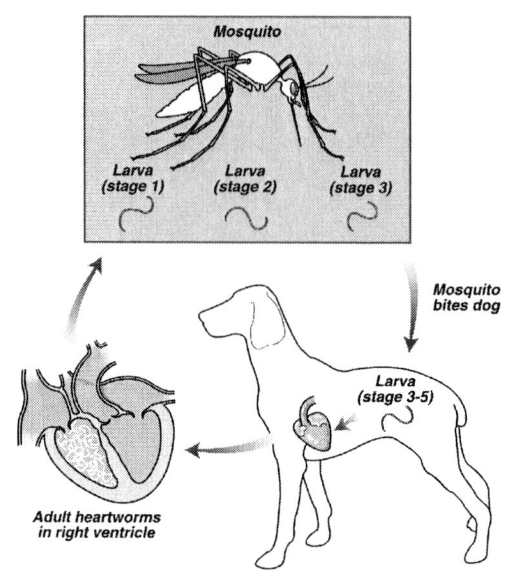

LIFE CYCLE OF THE HEARTWORM

As many as 30 species of mosquitoes can transmit heartworms. The female mosquito bites the infected dog and ingests the microfilariae during a blood meal. The microfilariae develop further for 10 to 30 days in the mosquito and then enter the mouth parts of the mosquito. The microfilariae are now called infective larvae because at this stage of development, they will grow to adulthood when they enter a dog. The mosquito bites the dog where the haircoat is thinnest. However, having long hair does not prevent a dog from getting heartworms.

When fully developed, the infective larvae enter the bloodstream and move to the heart and adjacent vessels, where they grow to maturity in 2 to 3 months and start reproducing, thereby completing the full life cycle.

Where are heartworms found?

Canine heartworm disease occurs all over the world. In the United States, it was once limited to the south and southeast regions. However, the disease is spreading and is now found in most regions of the United States and Canada, particularly where mosquitoes are prevalent.

How do dogs get infected with them?

The disease is not spread directly from dog to dog. An intermediate host, the mosquito, is required for transmission. Spread of the disease therefore coincides with the mosquito season. The number of dogs infected and the length of the mosquito season are directly correlated with the incidence of heartworm disease in any given area.

It takes a number of years before dogs show outward signs of infection. Consequently, the disease is diagnosed mostly in 4 to 8 year old dogs. The disease is seldom diagnosed in a dog under 1 year of age because the young worms (larvae) take up to 7 months to mature following establishment of infection in a dog.

What do heartworms do to the dog?

Adult worms

Adult worms cause disease by clogging the heart and major blood vessels leading from the heart. They interfere with the valve action in the heart. By clogging the main blood vessels, the blood supply to other organs of the body is reduced, particularly the lungs, liver and kidneys, leading to malfunction of these organs.

Most dogs infected with heartworms do not show any signs of disease for as long as two years. Unfortunately, by the time signs are seen, the disease is well advanced. The signs of heartworm disease depend on the number of adult worms present, the location of the worms, the length of time the worms have been present, and the degree of damage to the heart, lungs, liver, and kidneys from the adult worms and the microfilariae.

The most obvious signs are: a soft, dry, chronic cough, shortness of breath, weakness, nervousness, listlessness, and loss of stamina. All of these signs are most noticeable following exercise, when some dogs may even faint.

Listening to the chest with a stethoscope will often reveal abnormal lung and heart sounds. In advanced cases, congestive heart failure may be apparent and the abdomen and legs will swell from fluid accumulation. There may also be evidence of weight loss, poor condition, and anemia.

Severely infected dogs may die suddenly during exercise or excitement.

Microfilariae (young worms)

Microfilariae circulate throughout the body but remain primarily in the small blood vessels. Because they are as wide as the small vessels, they may block blood flow in these vessels. The body cells being supplied by these vessels are deprived of the nutrients and oxygen normally supplied by the blood. The lungs and liver are primarily affected.

Destruction of lung tissue leads to coughing. Cirrhosis of the liver causes jaundice, anemia, and general weakness because this organ is essential in maintaining a healthy animal. The kidneys may also be affected and allow poisons to accumulate in the body.

How is heartworm infection diagnosed?

In most cases, diagnosis of heartworm disease can be made by a blood test that can be run in the veterinary hospital. Further diagnostic procedures are essential, in advanced cases particularly, to determine if the dog can tolerate heartworm treatment. Depending on the case, some or all of the following procedures are recommended before treatment is started.

Serological test for antigens to adult heartworms

This is a test performed on a blood sample. It is the most widely used test because it detects antigens (proteins) produced by adult heartworms. It will be positive even if the dog does not have any microfilaria in the blood; this occurs about 20% of the time. Dogs with less than five adult heartworms will not have enough antigen to turn the test positive, so there may be some false negative results in early infections. Because the antigen detected is produced only by the female worm, a pure population of male heartworms will give a false negative, also. Therefore, there must be at least 5 female worms present for the most common test to be positive.

Blood test for microfilariae

A blood sample is examined under the microscope for the presence of microfilariae. If microfilariae are seen, the test is positive. The number of microfilariae seen gives us a general indication of the severity of the infection. However, the microfilariae are seen in greater numbers in the summer months and in the evening, so these variations must be considered. Approximately 20% of dogs do not test positive even though they have heartworms because of an acquired immunity to this stage of the heartworm. Because of this, the antigen test is the preferred test. Also, there is another microfilarial parasite which is fairly common in dogs; on the blood smear, these can be hard to distinguish from heartworm microfilariae.

Blood chemistries

Complete blood counts and blood tests for kidney and liver function may give an indirect indication of the presence of heartworm disease. These tests are also performed on dogs diagnosed as heartworm-infected to determine the function of the dog's organs prior to treatment.

Radiographs (X-rays)

A radiograph of a dog with heartworms will usually show heart enlargement and swelling of the large artery leading to the lungs from the heart. These signs are considered presumptive evidence of heartworm disease. Radiographs may also reveal the condition of the heart, lungs, and vessels. This information allows us to predict an increased possibility of complications related to treatment.

Electrocardiogram

An electrocardiogram (EKG) is a tracing of the electric currents generated by the heart. It is most useful to determine the presence of abnormal heart rhythms.

Echocardiography

An echocardiogram (Sonogram) allows us to see into the heart chambers and even visualize the heartworms themselves. Although somewhat expensive, this procedure can diagnose heartworms when other tests fail.

How are dogs treated for heartworms?

There is some risk involved in treating dogs with heartworms, although fatalities are rare. The drug that is used contains arsenic. The amount of arsenic is sufficient to kill heartworms without undue risk to the dog. However, dogs with poor liver or kidney function may have difficulty breaking down and eliminating the arsenic. In spite of this, more than 95% of dogs with heartworms are treated successfully.

Some dogs are seen with advanced heartworm disease. This means that the heartworms have been present long enough to cause substantial damage to the heart, lungs, blood vessels, kidneys, and liver. A few of these cases will be so far advanced that it will be safer to just treat the organ damage rather than risk treatment to kill the worms. Dogs in this condition are not likely to live more than a few weeks or months.

Treatment to kill adult worms

An injectable drug to kill adult heartworms is given for two days. It kills the adult heartworms in the heart and adjacent vessels over a period of about 30 days.

Complete rest is essential after treatment

Some adult worms die in a few days and start to decompose; the remainder will die within a month. As they break up, they are carried to the lungs, where they lodge in the small blood vessels and are eventually reabsorbed by the body. This is a dangerous period, and it is absolutely essential that the dog be kept quiet and not be allowed to exercise for 1 month following treatment. The first week after the injections is very critical because the worms are dying. A cough is noticeable for 7 to 8 weeks after treatment in many heavily infected dogs.

Prompt treatment is essential if the dog has a significant reaction in the weeks following the initial treatment, although such reactions are not common. If a dog shows loss of appetite, shortness of breath, severe coughing, coughing up blood, fever, and/or depression, your veterinarian should be notified. Response to antibiotics, cage rest, and supportive care, such as intravenous fluids, is usually good in these cases.

Treatment to kill microfilaria

Approximately one month following treatment to kill the adults, the dog is returned to the hospital for administration of a drug to kill microfilariae. Your dog needs to stay in the hospital for the day. Seven to ten days later a test is performed to determine if microfilariae are present. If they have been all killed, the treatment is complete. If there are still some present in the blood, treatment for microfilariae is repeated.

In some cases, the heartworm infection is "occult," meaning that no microfilariae were present. In this case, a follow-up treatment at one month is not needed.

Other treatments

In dogs with severe heartworm disease, it may be necessary to treat them with antibiotics, special diets, diuretics to remove fluid accumulations, and drugs to improve heart function prior to treatment for the heartworms.

Dogs with severe heart disease may need lifetime treatment for the failing heart, even after the heartworms have been killed. This includes the use of diuretics, heart drugs, aspirin, and special low salt, low protein diets.

Response to treatment

Dog owners are usually pleasantly surprised at the change in their dog following treatment for heartworms, especially if the dog had been showing signs of heartworm disease. The dog has a renewed vigor and vitality, improved appetite, and weight gain.

How can I prevent this from happening again?

When a dog has been successfully treated for heartworms, you cannot sit back and relax because dogs can be reinfected. Therefore, it is essential to begin a heartworm prevention program. There are three drugs which can be used to prevent heartworm infection. One is a daily, chewable tablet; the others are chewable tablets that are given only once monthly. All three products are very safe and very effective. Their costs are essentially identical. One of these should be started immediately after the treatment is completed.

HEMORRHAGIC GASTROENTERITIS

What is canine hemorrhagic gastroenteritis?

Hemorrhagic gastroenteritis (HGE) is a disorder of dogs which is usually fairly abrupt in onset. The significant signs of HGE are vomiting and/or diarrhea containing variable amounts of blood. The blood may be bright red (fresh blood) or dark (digested blood).

How is HGE diagnosed?

The diagnosis of HGE is one of exclusion, meaning other possible causes of bloody vomiting and/or bloody diarrhea must first be considered. Some of these possible causes include ulcers, trauma, gastrointestinal tumors or obstruction, foreign bodies, infectious diseases, and coagulation disorders. Evaluation of these other causes might require such tests as a complete blood count, biochemical analysis of the blood, urinalysis, x-rays, coagulation tests, fecal evaluation ultrasound or endoscopic (fiberoptic) evaluation of the gastrointestinal tract. Because the costs of all these tests could be significant, it is sometimes prudent to treat the dog for a few days with supportive care to see if the signs resolve. HGE is most common in small breeds of dogs. The blood count of affected dogs is frequently characterized by an elevated hematocrit (red blood cell count). Most normal dogs have hematocrits of 37 - 55%, while dogs with HGE may have hematocrits well above 60%. The elevated hematocrit provides the veterinarian with an important clue that the dog may have HGE.

What causes it?

The exact cause of HGE remains unknown.

How is it treated?

Dogs with HGE will appear profoundly ill and, if left untreated, may die. In most cases, the disorder appears to run its course in a few days if the animal is given appropriate supportive care. Intravenous fluid therapy provides the cornerstone of therapy for HGE. Fluids given under the skin are not considered adequate to meet the significant fluid requirements of most dogs with HGE.

If intravenous fluid therapy is not given, the dog's red blood count will continue to elevate due to dehydration. Eventually, the blood may become so thick that it flows very slowly through the blood vessels. In this situation, the dog is a prime candidate for a potentially fatal clotting disorder called disseminated intravascular coagulation (DIC). Once DIC has begun, it is often irreversible and may result in death.

Additional therapy may include antibiotics and anti-ulcer medication.

HEPATITIS (Infectious Canine Hepatitis)

What is 'hepatitis'?

Hepatitis means inflammation of the liver. As a specific disease, infectious canine hepatitis, is a viral infection caused by a member of the Adenovirus family.

Does it affect other animals or people?

Other members of the dog family, foxes for example, can be infected, but it is harmless to people.

How is the virus spread?

The hepatitis virus is transmitted in urine or nose and eye secretions of infected animals, and then through direct contact with these infected materials by a susceptible dog. Young dogs are at highest risk, and signs of disease usually occur within 2 to 5 days, but the incubation period can be as long as 14 days. In older dogs some infections may go unnoticed or be mild.

What are the clinical signs?

In the mild form the dog may be merely off food, depressed and have a fever. Some of these cases develop an opacity of one or both corneas of their eyes (so-called 'blue eye') one to two weeks later.

Some dogs have respiratory signs - eye and nose discharges and cough - indistinguishable from other forms of kennel cough (*see* p. 94).

In severe cases, usually puppies, other than the fever, depression and loss of appetite, there is abdominal pain, vomiting, diarrhea, puffy edema (subcutaneous fluid swelling) of the head and neck, and possible jaundice. Such cases are often fatal.

What is the treatment?

As with most viral infections there is no specific treatment. Antibiotics are ineffective against viruses. Treatment is aimed at reducing symptoms, and giving time for the dog's immune system to respond. This includes rest, intravenous fluids and medication to reduce the severe symptoms.

What about vaccination?

Vaccination is very successful, and is routinely administered in puppy vaccination programs. The protection conferred lasts for many months, but it does decrease with time. Therefore annual revaccination is recommended.

What is hip dysplasia?

Hip dysplasia is defined as a deformity of the coxofemoral (hip) joint that occurs during the growth period. Hip dysplasia is a hereditary condition that creates a poorly fitting hip joint. As the dog walks on this joint, arthritis will eventually develop, causing pain in the joint. The degree of lameness that occurs is usually dependent upon the extent of arthritic changes in the hip joint.

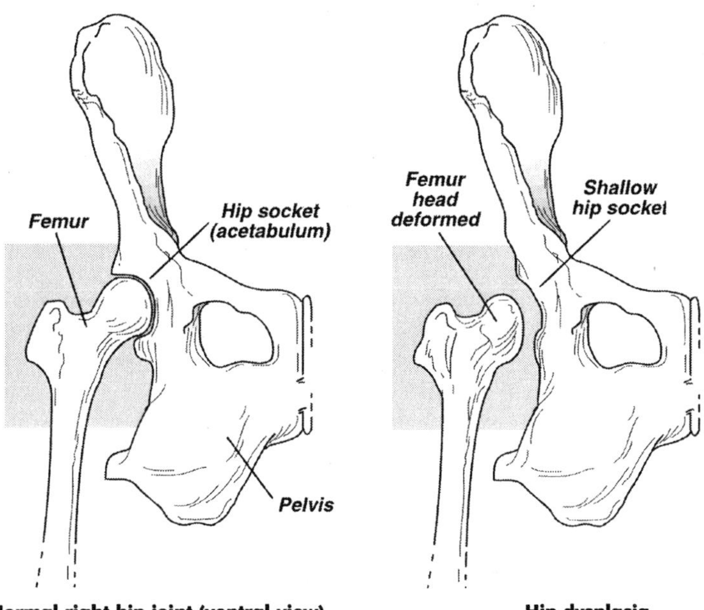

Normal right hip joint (ventral view) **Hip dysplasia**

Is this found in certain breeds of dogs?

Most breeds of dogs can be affected with hip dysplasia although it is predominantly seen in the larger breeds of dogs, such as the German Shepherd, St. Bernard, Labrador Retriever, Pointers, and Setters. There is equal distribution of the disease between male and female dogs.

What are the clinical signs, and when do they occur?

The typical clinical signs of hip dysplasia are rear leg pain, lack of coordination, and a reluctance to rise. Wasting of the large muscle groups in the rear limbs may eventually develop. Most owners report that the dog has had difficulty in rising from a lying position for a period of weeks or months; lameness and pain subsequently develop. Again, the severity of signs and progression of the disease usually correlate with the extent of arthritis in the joint. Clinical signs can occur as early as 4 - 6 weeks of age, but most dogs manifest the disease as a lameness around one to two years of age. Dogs with mild hip dysplasia and minimal arthritis may not become lame and in pain until 6 - 10 years of age.

How is it diagnosed?

Tentative diagnosis of hip dysplasia is made on the basis of history, breed, and clinical signs. A large breed dog that has been slow to rise for several months and now is lame is highly suspect for hip dysplasia; a dog which refuses to rise should also be considered a candidate. Because the clinical signs may mimic other diseases, final diagnosis of hip dysplasia can only be made on the basis of specific radiographic (x-ray) findings. To obtain the proper radiographs, dogs must be carefully positioned on the radiographic table. This procedure requires the use of a short-acting anesthetic. The radiographs are evaluated for abnormal shape of the hip joint and for degenerative changes (arthritis).

How is it treated?

The degree of clinical signs and arthritic changes in the joints determine the specific approach to therapy. Treatment of hip dysplasia may involve the use of drugs or surgery, or both. The options are as follows:

Anti-inflammatory drugs

Several drugs will give relief from pain. Aspirin or acetaminophen may work well in some dogs. Other steroidal (cortisone) and non-steroidal drugs may also be used. Most have some side-effects and most require administration once or twice daily. Many dogs have severe stomach irritation to ibuprofen, so this drug is not recommended. Unfortunately, it is not possible to predict which dog will respond to which drug. Therefore, a series of trials may be needed to find the most effective one for your dog. Extreme caution is advised when these drugs are given to dogs with a history of kidney disease or with marginal kidney function. Many of these drugs have an adverse effect on blood flow to the kidneys and can lead to kidney failure. This does not appear to be a concern if kidney function is normal.

As alluded to above, dogs with a history of ulcers are also at risk for complications. Your veterinarian can determine the risk for your dog. Anti-inflammatory drug therapy is most often used in older dogs, in dogs that did not get good relief from surgery, or in dogs for which surgery is not feasible.

Surgery

There are four main procedures: pectineal myotomy (muscle cutting surgery), femoral head ostectomy (ball removal), triple osteotomy, and hip joint replacement.

- Pectineal myotomy is a relatively minor procedure that involves cutting a small muscle that puts pressure on the hip joint. It results in no loss of leg function and gives good to excellent relief in 80 - 90% of dogs. If both hips are abnormal, both hips may be operated on at the same time. The dog recovers from surgery in one to two days. However, this procedure does not stabilize the hip joint or prevent progression of arthritic changes. Within a few months to several years, pain and lameness will return.

- Femoral head ostectomy (FHO) is another choice. The hip joint is a ball and socket joint. FHO is the removal of the ball part of the joint. This gives excellent results in small dogs because a functional "false joint" forms. However, some large dogs may not form this "false joint" very well. This procedure is usually used in large dogs if arthritis is very severe, if the hip dislocates, or if the expense of the other procedures is prohibitive.

- Triple osteotomy is a procedure in which the pelvis is cut in three places around the hip joint. The bone is rotated to create better alignment with the femoral head (the ball). It is reattached so that the joint functions in a more normal fashion without looseness and pain. This should only be performed in a dog with no arthritic changes in the joint. It is an expensive procedure.

- Hip joint transplant (hip replacement) is possible, as is done in humans. A stainless steel ball and socket are attached to the pelvis and femur in place of the abnormal ones. It is another expensive procedure, but it may give many years of pain-free use of the hips. Although the intent is for the transplant to be permanent, the new joint may loosen after a period of time.

I am considering breeding my dog. Can anything be done to prevent hip dysplasia in the puppies?

Research has shown that the cause of hip dysplasia is related to a combination of genetic and environmental factors. The disease is known to be an inherited condition and the genetics of hip dysplasia are extremely complicated. In addition, environmental factors such as overfeeding and excessive exercise can predispose a dog (especially growing puppies) to developing hip dysplasia. Because the inheritance of the disease is so complicated, many questions remain regarding eradication of the disease.

Here are some practical suggestions:

- Have your dog radiographed before breeding to be sure the hips are normal. ***If they are not, this dog should not be bred.***

- Consider a feeding program to slow growth. There is a growing body of evidence indicating that dogs that grow very rapidly are more likely to have hip dysplasia. Many authorities recommend feeding an adult-type food to puppies of high risk breeds so their growth is slower. They will still reach their full genetic body size, but just not as rapidly.

- Avoid excessive exercise in a growing puppy. Any abnormality in the structure of the hip joint is magnified if excessive running and jumping occur. It is not necessary to treat your puppy as if it were handicapped, but long sessions of running or chasing thrown objects can be detrimental to joints.

What does it mean to have the hips certified as normal?

The Orthopedic Foundation for Animals (O.F.A.) is an organization established for the purpose of standardizing the evaluation process of canine hip radiographs. The O.F.A. consists of a board of certified veterinary radiologists who are skilled in detecting hip dysplasia. If the radiographs submitted to the O.F.A. are declared normal, the dog is issued an O.F.A. certificate number indicating that it has normal hip confirmation. The O.F.A. requires that dogs must be a minimum of two years of age to be certified. Many breeders require that a dog must have an O.F.A. certificate before breeding is allowed.

Another hip evaluation program is called the PennHip method. Radiographs are made of the anesthetized dog in such a manner as to place outward force on the hip joints. This can reveal looseness in the joints that may elude detection by the more standard radiographic methods. It is also useful in identifying hip dysplasia in puppies as young as 4 months of age. Although any veterinarian can make the appropriate radiographs and submit them for O.F.A. certification, the PennHip method must be performed by a veterinarian specifically trained and certified in this procedure.

HOOKWORM INFECTION

What are hookworms?

Hookworms are parasites which get their name from the hook-like mouthparts they use to attach to the intestinal wall. They are only about 1/8" (3 mm) long and so small in diameter that you have to be looking very carefully to see them. Despite their small size, they suck large amounts of blood from the tiny vessels in the intestinal wall. A large number of hookworms can cause anemia. This problem is most common in puppies, but it will occasionally occur in adult dogs. In general, dogs tend to harbor very few hookworms compared to the number carried by infected dogs.

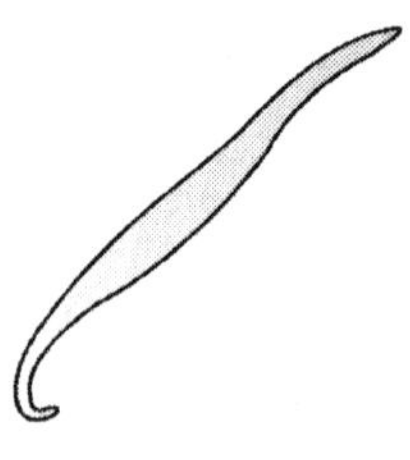

Hookworm (3x actual size)

How did my dog get hookworms?

Dogs may become infected with hookworms by four routes: orally, through the skin, through the mother's placenta before birth, and through the mother's milk. A dog may become infected when it swallows hookworm larvae (immature worm). The larvae may also penetrate the skin and migrate to the intestine to mature and complete its life cycle. If a pregnant dog has hookworms, the pregnancy may reactivate larvae. These larvae will enter the female's circulation and pass to the puppy through the placental blood flow. Finally, puppies may become infected through the mother's milk. This is considered to be an important route of infection for puppies.

What kinds of problems do hookworms cause for my dog?

The most significant problems appear related to intestinal distress and anemia. Blood loss results from the parasites sucking blood from intestinal capillaries. The presence of pale gums, diarrhea, or weakness might suggest the need to specifically determine the dog's red blood cell count. Some dogs experience significant weight loss, bloody diarrhea, or failure to grow properly with hookworm infection. Skin irritation and itching can be one of the common signs of a heavily infested environment. The larvae burrow into the skin and cause the dog a great deal of itching and discomfort.

How is hookworm infection diagnosed?

Hookworms are diagnosed with a microscopic examination of a small stool sample. Since there are so many eggs produced on a daily basis, they are rather easily detected. One adult female hookworm is reported to produce as many as 20,000 eggs a day! In puppies, large numbers of worms usually must be present before eggs are shed into the stool. For this reason, fecal examination may be less reliable in very young puppies than in adult dogs.

How are the hookworms treated?

There are several very effective drugs that will kill hookworms. These are given by injection or orally and have few, if any, side-effects. However, these drugs only kill the adult hookworms. Therefore, it is necessary to treat again in about 2 - 4 weeks to kill any newly formed adult worms that were larvae at the time of the first treatment.

A blood transfusion may be necessary in some dogs because of the rather severe anemia which can be produced.

Since the dog's environment can be laden with hookworm eggs and larvae, it may be necessary to treat it with a chemical to kill them. There are some available that are safe to use on grass.

Are canine hookworms infectious to people?

Adult hookworms do not infect humans; however, the larvae can burrow into human skin. This causes itching, commonly called ground itch, but the worms do not mature into adults. Direct contact of human skin to moist, hookworm infested soil is required. Fortunately, this does not occur very often if normal hygiene practices are observed.

In rare instances, the canine hookworm will penetrate into deeper tissues and partially mature in the human intestine. A few reports of hookworm enterocolitis (small and large intestinal inflammation) have occurred in the recent past.

What can be done to control hookworm infection in dogs and to prevent human infection?

All pups should be treated at 2 - 3 weeks of age.

- Prompt deworming should be given when parasites are detected; periodic deworming may be appropriate for pets at high risk for reinfection.

- Prompt disposal of dog feces should occur, especially in yards, playgrounds, and public parks.

- Strict hygiene is important, especially for children. Do not allow children to play in potentially contaminated environments.

- Nursing females should be treated concurrently with their pups; nursing may reactivate infection in the female.

- Most heartworm prevention products contain a drug that will prevent hookworm infections. However, these products will not kill the adult hookworms, so dogs must be treated for adult hookworms first.

HYPOTHYROIDISM

What is the thyroid gland, and what does it do?

The thyroid gland is one of the most important glands in the body. It is located in the neck near the trachea and is composed of two lobes, one on each side of the trachea (windpipe). This gland is controlled by the body's master gland, the pituitary gland, located at the base of the brain.

The thyroid gland regulates the rate of metabolism. If it is hyperfunctional, metabolism speeds up. If it is less functional than normal, metabolism slows down. The latter is the basis for the clinical signs of hypothyroidism.

What causes hypothyroidism?

Hypothyroidism is almost always caused by one of two diseases: lymphocytic thyroiditis or idiopathic thyroid gland atrophy. The former disease is the most common cause of hypothyroidism and is thought to be an immune-mediated disease. This means that the immune system decides that the thyroid is abnormal or foreign and attacks it. It is not known why the immune system does this. Idiopathic thyroid gland atrophy is also poorly understood. Normal thyroid tissue is replaced by fat tissue in what is considered a degenerative disease.

These two causes of hypothyroidism account for more than 95% of the cases. The other five percent are due to uncommon diseases, including cancer of the thyroid gland.

What are the clinical signs?

When the rate of metabolism slows down, virtually every organ in the body is affected in some manner. Most affected dogs have one or more of several "typical" physical and/or chemical abnormalities. These include:

- Weight gain without an increase in appetite
- Lethargy and lack of desire to exercise
- Cold intolerance (gets cold easily)

- Dry haircoat with excessive shedding
- Very thin haircoat to near baldness
- Increased pigmentation in the skin
- Increased susceptibility to skin and ear infections
- Failure to re-grow hair after clipping or shaving
- High blood cholesterol

Some dogs also have other abnormalities that are not the typical findings. These include:

- Thickening of the facial skin so they have a "tragic facial expression"
- Abnormal function of nerves causing non-painful lameness, dragging of feet, lack of coordination, and a head tilt
- Loss of libido and infertility in intact males
- Lack of heat periods, infertility, and abortion in females
- Fat deposits in the corneas of the eyes
- Keratoconjunctivitis sicca ("dry eye" due to very thick tears)

How is it diagnosed?

The most common test is the T_4 level. This is a measurement of the main thyroid hormone in a blood sample. If it is below normal and the correct clinical signs are present, the test is meaningful. However, testing for the T_4 level can be misleading because some dogs that are not hypothyroid may have subnormal levels. This happens when another disease is present or when certain drugs are given. If hypothyroidism is suspected but the T_4 is normal, other tests can be performed. These are more expensive so they are not used as first line tests.

Can it be treated?

Hypothyroidism is treatable but not curable. It is treated with oral administration of a thyroid replacement hormone. This drug must be given for the rest of the dog's life.

How is the proper dose determined?

There is a standard dose that is used initially; it is based on the dog's weight. However, after about one month of treatment, further testing is done to verify that the thyroid hormone levels are normal. In some dogs, the dose will need to be further adjusted every 6 - 12 months.

What happens if the medication is overdosed?

Signs of hyperthyroidism can be caused. These include hyperactivity, lack of sleep, weight loss, and an increase in water consumption. If any of these occur, notify your veterinarian so that a proper adjustment can be made.

ICTERUS

What is icterus?

Icterus is also known as jaundice or yellow jaundice. It means that a yellow pigment is found in the blood and in the tissues. It is most easily seen in the gingiva (gums), the sclerae (white part of the eyes), and the pinnae (ear flaps). However, if these tissues normally have a dark color, icterus will probably not be seen.

What causes icterus?

The causes of icterus fall into three major categories:

- **Destruction of red blood cells**

  The process of red cell destruction is known as hemolysis. It can occur within blood vessels (intravascular) or in the spleen and liver (extravascular).

- **Liver disease**

  Any disease that causes destruction of liver cells or causes bile to become trapped in the liver can cause icterus.

- **Obstruction of the bile duct**

  The bile duct carries an important fluid for digestion, bile, from the gall bladder to the small intestine. Obstruction can occur within the gall bladder or anywhere along the bile duct.

How is the exact cause determined?

Within each category listed above are several possible causes. Determining the cause of icterus requires a series of tests. Some of these tests determine which category is involved. Once that is known, other tests are done to look for a specific disease which is leading to the icteric state.

What tests determine hemolysis?

Since hemolysis results in red blood cell destruction, determination of red blood cell numbers is one of the first tests performed on the icteric patient. There are three tests that may be used for this. The **red blood cell count** is an actual machine count of red blood cells. The **packed cell volume (PCV)** is a centrifuge-performed test that separates the red blood cells from the serum or plasma (the liquid parts of the blood). The **hematocrit** is another way to determine if there is a reduced number of red blood cells. All three of these tests are part of a complete blood count (CBC).

What causes hemolysis?

Hemolysis can be caused by toxic plants, chemicals or drugs, parasites on the red blood cells, heartworms, autoimmune diseases, and cancer. Several tests are needed to determine which of these is the cause.

What tests determine the presence of liver disease?

A chemistry profile is performed on dogs with icterus. This is a group of 20 - 30 tests that are performed on a blood sample. The chemistry profile contains several tests that are specific for liver disease. The main ones are the alanine aminotransferase (ALT), aspartate aminotransferase (AST), alkaline phosphatase (ALP), and total bilirubin. If these tests are normal, and there is reason to suspect liver disease, a bile acid analysis is performed.

Although each of these look at the liver from a slightly different perspective, ultimately they only determine that liver disease is occurring. None of them are able to determine the exact cause of the disease. To make that determination, a biopsy of the liver is necessary. This can be done in three ways.

1) **Fine-needle aspirate**

   To perform this procedure, a small gauge needle is inserted through the skin into the liver. A syringe is used to aspirate some cells from the liver. The cells are placed on a glass slide, stained, and studied under a microscope. This is the least invasive and quickest test, but it has certain limitations. Because only a few cells are obtained, it is possible that a representative sample from the liver will not be obtained. It is also not possible to view the cells in their normal relationship to each other (i.e., tissue architecture). Some diseases can be diagnosed with this technique, and others cannot.

2) **Needle biopsy**

   This procedure is similar to the fine-needle aspirate except a much larger needle is used. This needle is able to recover a core of tissue, not just a few cells. The sample is fixed in formaldehyde and submitted to a pathologist for analysis. General anesthesia is required, but the dog is anesthetized for only a very short period of time. If it is done properly and with a little luck, this procedure will recover a very meaningful sample. However, the veterinarian cannot choose the exact site of the liver to biopsy because the liver is not visible. Therefore, it is still possible to miss the abnormal tissue.

3) **Surgical wedge biopsy**

   The dog is placed under general anesthesia, and the abdomen is opened surgically. This permits direct visualization of the liver so the exact site for biopsy can be chosen. A piece of the liver is surgically removed using a scalpel. This approach gives the most reliable biopsy sample, but the stress of surgery and the expense are the greatest of all of the biopsy methods.

What causes liver disease?

The most common causes of liver disease include bacterial infections, viral infections, toxic plants, chemicals or drugs, cancer, autoimmune diseases, and certain breed-specific liver diseases.

What tests determine bile duct obstruction?

Dogs with obstructed bile ducts are usually extremely icteric. Their yellow color can often be seen readily in the skin, as well as the sclerae and gingiva. However, an evaluation of the gall bladder and bile duct is necessary to be sure that obstruction is present. An ultrasound examination is the most accurate non-invasive way to evaluate the gall bladder and bile duct. This technology uses sound waves to "look" at the liver, gall bladder, and bile duct. If this is not available, radiographs (x-rays) should be taken of the liver. However, sometimes exploratory surgery is necessary to properly evaluate the dog for biliary obstruction.

What causes bile duct obstruction?

The most common causes of bile duct obstruction include pancreatitis, trauma, cancer, gall bladder stones, and severely thickened bile.

How is icterus treated?

Icterus is not a disease; it is a sign that disease is present. Therefore, there is not a specific treatment for icterus. Icterus will resolve when the disease that causes it is cured.

The basis for resolving icterus is to diagnose the underlying disease. When the proper testing is done, this is usually possible. Then, treatment can begin.

INFLAMMATORY BOWEL DISEASE

What is inflammatory bowel disease?

Inflammatory Bowel Disease (IBD) is a chronic disease of the intestinal tract. Occasionally, the stomach may be involved. Most affected dogs have a history of recurrent or chronic vomiting and/or diarrhea. During periods of vomiting or diarrhea, the dog may lose weight but is generally normal in other ways. As a rule, most affected dogs eat well (or even have an increased appetite) and appear normal.

What causes this disease?

The cause of IBD is poorly understood. In fact, it appears that there may be several causes. Whatever the cause(s), the end result is that the lining of the intestine is invaded by inflammatory cells. An allergic-type response is then set in place within the bowel lining. This interferes with the ability of the dog to digest and absorb nutrients. For some dogs, dietary components are speculated to play a role in initiation of the disease. Bacterial proteins may be involved in other cases. In most instances, an underlying cause cannot be identified.

How is IBD diagnosed?

There are two ways to diagnose IBD. A biopsy of the affected part of the stomach or intestine will allow identification of this disease. The preferred diagnostic approach utilizes a flexible endoscope which allows access to the lining of the stomach, small intestine, and colon. If the site of inflammation involves any of these locations, a confirmed diagnosis is achieved.

Sometimes, the small intestine may be difficult to enter in very small dogs because its opening is very narrow; in these cases, surgical biopsy may be needed. Fortunately, this is rarely needed.

In some cases, diagnosis may be assisted by a therapeutic trial involving administration of particular drugs, along with certain dietary changes. Since not all dogs respond to the same drugs, the trial may involve a series of several drugs and may take several weeks. Also, several different diets may be tried, depending on which part of the bowel appears most involved. These diets include hypoallergenic foods, low residue diets, or high fiber foods. The dog is monitored during the therapeutic trial for a decrease in clinical signs and, in some cases, weight gain.

Is IBD treatable?

When a diagnosis of IBD is made, the dog is placed on a hypoallergenic, low residue or high fiber diet for eight weeks or more. This helps to identify the contribution of dietary components to the problem. Although this is not a common cause of the disease, it is easy to treat if an acceptable food is found. If the dietary trial does not offer any improvement, medication is used to control (not cure) the problem. Since not all dogs respond to the same medication, a series of drug trials may be necessary.

What is the prognosis?

Once the appropriate drugs or diet can be determined, many dogs are maintained on these for life, although dosages of the drugs may eventually be decreased. Occasionally, a dog will be able to stop drug therapy at some point.

Most dogs do well for many years; others require alterations in therapy every few months. Unfortunately, a few dogs will ultimately become totally resistant to treatment.

Some severe forms of canine inflammatory bowel disease will eventually progress to intestinal cancer. This finding is well documented in human beings and, in recent years, it has become apparent that this occurs in dogs, as well.

What are allergies, and how do they affect dogs?

One of the most common conditions affecting dogs is allergy. In the allergic state, the dog's immune system "overreacts" to foreign substances (allergens or antigens) to which it is exposed. These overreactions are manifested in three ways. The most common is itching of the skin, either localized (one area) or generalized (all over the dog). Another manifestation involves the respiratory system and may result in coughing, sneezing, and/or wheezing. Sometimes, there may be an associated nasal or ocular (eye) discharge. The third manifestation involves the digestive system, resulting in vomiting or diarrhea.

Aren't there several types of allergies?

There are five known types of allergies in the dog: contact, flea (*see* p. 63), food (*see* p. 69), bacterial, and inhalant. Each of these has some common expressions in dogs, and each has some unique features.

What is inhalant allergy?

The most common type of allergy is the inhalant type, also known as atopy. Dogs may be allergic to all of the same inhaled allergens that affect humans. These include tree pollens (cedar, ash, oak, etc.), grass pollens (especially Bermuda), weed pollens (ragweed, etc.), molds, mildew, and the house dust mite. Many of these allergies occur seasonally, such as ragweed, cedar, and grass pollens. However, others are with us all the time, such as molds, mildew, and house dust mites.

What happens when a dog inhales something to which it is allergic?

When humans inhale allergens, we express the allergy as respiratory problems. These include coughing, sneezing, a runny nose, and watery eyes. The dog's reaction, however, usually produces severe, generalized itching. It will chew, lick, or scratch almost any area of the body, including the feet. Chewing and scratching produce hair loss and inflamed areas of the skin. Saliva will stain light colored hair, so dogs that lick excessively will have orange or reddish brown hair. This is often seen on the feet. Although most people think that itching is related to fleas, the most common cause of itching in the dog is inhalant allergy.

What is causing my dog's allergy?

That is not a question that can be answered easily. The itching produced by ragweed allergy is the same as that produced by oak pollen allergy. In other words, an individual animal or person can be allergic to many different things with the end result (itching) being the same. In some cases, allergy testing can make specific determinations, and sometimes an educated guess can be accurate if the itching corresponds with the blooming season of certain plants. However, it is not always necessary to know the specific allergen for treatment to be successful.

What is meant by "seasonal allergy" and "year round allergy?"

As the names imply, some dogs only have allergic reactions during specific periods of the year. Others will itch year round. A year round allergy occurs for two reasons. First, the allergen is present year round. This is the case for indoor dogs that are allergic to house dust mites, also known as "house dust." Second, the dog is allergic to so many things that at least one of those allergens is present at all times.

My dog seemed to have a seasonal allergy for several years, and now it seems year round. Is that possible?

Not only is that possible, it is almost expected. As the dog ages, it usually becomes allergic to more and more things. After several years of acquiring new allergies, it reaches the point that it is constantly exposed to something to which it is allergic.

My dog seems to have a grass allergy. Does that mean it should not walk on grass?

No. Dogs that are allergic to "grass", for example, are really allergic to grass pollen. The blades of grass will cause no harm to your dog. Bermuda grass is the most allergenic grass because it releases so much pollen into the air. Keeping it mowed so it does not pollinate seems logical, but your neighbors must do the same because the pollen is airborne. The same principle applies to trees. Dogs are not allergic to the wood of a certain tree, only to its pollen.

How is inhalant allergy treated?

Treatment depends largely on the length of the dog's allergy season and involves four approaches:

- **Anti-inflammatory drugs**

  Anti-inflammatory therapy will dramatically block the allergic reaction in most cases. Steroids ("cortisone") may be given orally or by injection, depending on the circumstances. If steroids are appropriate for your dog, you will be instructed in their proper use. Antihistamines can be of value in treating the allergic dog when they are combined with steroids. In some dogs, antihistamines can significantly decrease the amount of steroid needed to provide relief. Fatty acid supplementation can also be implemented with steroids and antihistamines. When the three of them are combined, most allergic dogs are significantly improved. This is a non-specific approach which does not treat the allergy, only the result of the allergic state (itching).

- **Shampoo therapy**

  Many dogs are helped considerably by frequent bathing with a hypoallergenic shampoo. It has been demonstrated that some allergens may be absorbed through the skin. Frequent bathing is thought to reduce the amount of antigen exposure through this route. In addition to removing surface antigen, bathing alone will provide some temporary relief from itching and may allow the use of a lower dose of steroids.

Some of the hypoallergenic shampoos incorporate fatty acids; these may be absorbed through the skin and offer a localized anti-inflammatory action. The role of the fatty acids in allergy treatment is an area of active research interest in veterinary medicine.

- **Antibiotics**

  Dogs that damage their skin by licking, chewing, and scratching are quite susceptible to bacterial infections in the skin. If this occurs, antibiotics should be given until the infection is controlled. The skin infection itself can be quite irritating and cause a dog to itch even more.

- **Hyposensitization**

  The third major form of allergy treatment is hyposensitization with specific antigen injections (or "allergy shots"). Once testing identifies the specific allergens, very small amounts of the antigen are injected weekly. The purpose of this therapy is to reprogram the body's immune system. It is hoped that as time passes, the immune system will become less reactive to the problem-causing allergens. If hyposensitization appears to help the dog, injections will continue for several years. For most dogs, a realistic goal is for the itching to be significantly reduced in severity; in some dogs, itching may completely resolve. Generally, steroids are only used on a brief and intermittent basis. This therapeutic approach is recommended for the middle-aged or older dog that has year round itching caused by inhalant allergy.

  Although hyposensitization is the ideal way to treat inhalant allergy, it does have some drawbacks and may not be the best choice in certain circumstances and for these reasons:

  Cost: This is the most expensive form of treatment.

  Age of Patient: Because many dogs develop additional allergies as they get older, young dogs may need to be retested 1 - 3 years later.

  Success Rate: About 50% of dogs will have an excellent response, about 25% get partial to good response, and the remaining 25% get little or no response. The same statistics are true for people undergoing hyposensitization.

  Food Allergies: Although tests for food allergy are available, the reliability of these tests is so low that it is not recommended at this time. A food trial remains the best diagnostic test for food allergy.

  Time of Response: The time until apparent response may be 2 - 5 months, or longer.

  Interference of steroids: Dogs must not receive oral steroids for 2 weeks or injectable steroids for 6 weeks prior to testing; these drugs will interfere with the test results.

My dog has fleas. Couldn't that be causing the itching?

A dog with inhalant allergy will itch even if fleas are not present. However, if fleas are crawling around on your dog, the itching will increase. Although getting rid of all of your dog's fleas will not stop the itching, it will make it much easier to control the itching successfully (*see* 'Fleas' p. 63).

My dog has a terrible odor. Is that related?

There are two possible causes of odor associated with inhalant allergy. These dogs are very prone to ear infections because the ear canal is an extension of the skin. When it becomes inflamed, it is easily infected. These dogs are also likely to have seborrhea. Sebum is the oily material normally produced in the skin. When a dog scratches, sebum production increases dramatically. This produces a musty odor. A bath will remove the odor, but it is gone for only a few hours. The key to controlling seborrhea is to stop the itching and scratching.

Is there another disease that can be part of my dog's problem?

Yes. Hypothyroidism is a disease in which the thyroid gland does not produce enough thyroid hormone. This has many effects on the body because it controls the rate of metabolism. Hypothyroid dogs frequently have abnormalities of the skin and haircoat. Skin infections (which themselves may increase itching) are common with this hormonal disorder and may aggravate allergic conditions.

How is hypothyroidism diagnosed and treated?

A simple blood test will make the diagnosis in most dogs. However, for some dogs, the thyroid value falls into a "gray zone," and further testing of the thyroid gland is necessary to confirm a diagnosis. Sometimes, illness will cause a dog to have low thyroid values when hypothyroidism is not really present. Hypothyroidism can be treated with thyroid replacement hormone tablets. Without treatment for this disease, treatment for inhalant allergy is more difficult.

The itching did not stop as expected. What does that mean?

There are two scenarios in which there will be disappointing results. The first scenario is when tablets are given and the response is poor. A few dogs will respond better to injectable steroids than to the oral form. Fortunately, this only occurs about 5% of the time. However, successful management of itching in those dogs will require periodic injections of steroids, if the itching cannot be controlled with other drugs or other forms of treatment.

The other scenario is either a total failure to respond to injectable or oral steroids or a response to an injection is short-lived, lasting only a few days instead of a few weeks. This could occur because the dose was too low; however, it may also mean that the dog has food allergy.

Food allergy causes itching and scratching identical to inhalant allergy, but it responds very poorly to steroids. Food allergy is diagnosed with a food trial using a hypoallergenic diet.

KENNEL COUGH (Tracheobronchitis)

What is Kennel Cough?

Kennel Cough is a broad term covering any infectious or contagious condition of dogs where coughing is a feature. The term tracheobronchitis describes the location of the infection (windpipe and bronchial tubes). Several viruses and bacteria can be involved. These include adenovirus type-2 (distinct from the adenovirus type 1 which causes infectious hepatitis *see* p. 78); parainfluenza virus, and the bacterium *Bordetella bronchiseptica.* Because the infection spreads when dogs are housed together, it is often seen soon after dogs have been in kennels, hence the name.

What are the signs, besides the cough?

They are quite variable. It is often a mild disease, but the cough may persist. Signs include runny eyes and nose, swollen tonsils, wheezing respiration, lack of appetite and depressed behavior.

What is the treatment?

There is no specific treatment for the viral infections, but many of the more severe signs are due to bacterial involvement, particularly *Bordetella.* Antibiotics are useful against these bacteria, although some resistance to certain antibiotics has occurred. Some cases are quite stubborn to treat, but most infections clear within a week, 3 weeks at most. Mild signs may linger even when the bacteria have been eliminated.

How can I prevent my dog contracting Kennel Cough?

Most vaccination programs your veterinarian will recommend contain adenovirus and parainfluenza. *Bordetella* vaccination is also becoming more widely recommended.

How effective are these vaccines?

Immunity, after natural infection with respiratory viruses like parainfluenza, or bacteria like *Bordetella,* is neither solid nor long-lasting. We cannot expect vaccines to do much better. Therefore it is sometimes recommended to give a booster dose, particularly of *Bordetella* vaccine, shortly before a scheduled period in kennels.

How are the Bordetella vaccines delivered?

Bordetella vaccination is performed either by injection or more recently by the "intra-nasal" route. Intra-nasal refers to the liquid vaccine being delivered as nose drops. This allows local immunity to develop on the mucous membranes of the nose, throat and windpipe where the infectious agents first attack.

What is meant by the term "Kidney Failure"?

The term "kidney failure" suggests that the kidneys have quit working and are, therefore, not making urine. However, by definition, kidney failure is the inability of the kidneys to remove waste products from the blood. This definition can occasionally create confusion because some will equate kidney failure with failure to make urine. Kidney failure is NOT the inability to make urine. Ironically, most dogs in kidney failure are actually producing large quantities of urine, but the body's wastes are not being effectively eliminated. It is typically a condition of relatively slow progression from onset and long-standing (chronic).

When is this likely to happen in my dog?

The typical form of kidney failure is the result of aging; it is simply a "wearing out" process. The age of onset is related to the size of the dog. For most small dogs, the early signs occur at about 10 - 14 years of age. However, large dogs have a shorter age span and may go into kidney failure as early as 7 years of age.

What changes are likely to occur in my dog?

The kidneys are nothing more than filters. When aging causes the filtration process to become inefficient and ineffective, blood flow to the kidneys is increased in an attempt to increase filtration. This results in the production of more urine. To keep the dog from becoming dehydrated due to increased fluid loss in the urine, thirst is increased; this results in more water consumption. Thus, the early clinical signs of kidney failure are increased water consumption and increased urine production. The clinical signs of more advanced kidney failure include loss of appetite, depression, vomiting, diarrhea, and very bad breath. Occasionally, ulcers will be found in the mouth. When kidney failure is accompanied by these clinical signs, it is called uremia.

How is chronic kidney failure diagnosed?

The diagnosis of kidney failure is made by determining the level of two waste products in the blood: blood urea nitrogen (BUN) and blood creatinine. The urinalysis is also needed to complete the study of kidney function. Although BUN and creatinine levels reflect kidney failure, they do not predict it. A dog with marginal kidney function may have normal blood tests. If that dog is stressed with major illness or surgery, the kidneys may fail, sending the blood test values up quickly.

Since this is basically just a wearing out process, can it be treated with anything other than a kidney transplant?

In some cases, the kidneys are worn out so that they cannot be revived. However, with aggressive treatment many dogs will live for several more months or years. Treatment occurs in two phases. The first phase is to "restart" the kidneys. Large quantities of intravenous fluids are given to "flush out" the kidneys. This flushing process, called diuresis, helps to stimulate the kidney cells to function again. If enough functional kidney cells remain, they may be able to adequately meet the body's needs for waste removal. Fluid therapy includes replacement of various electrolytes, especially potassium. Other important aspects of initial treatment include proper nutrition and drugs to control vomiting and diarrhea.

What can I expect from this phase of treatment?

There are three possible outcomes from the first phase of treatment:

1) The kidneys will resume functioning and continue to function for a few weeks to a few years.

2) The kidneys will resume functioning during treatment but fail again as soon as treatment stops.

3) Kidney function will not return. Unfortunately, there are no reliable tests that will predict the outcome.

If the first phase of treatment is successful, what happens next?

The second phase of treatment is to keep the kidneys functioning as long as possible. This is accomplished with one or more of the following, depending on the situation:

- **A low protein diet**

  This helps to keep the blood tests as close to normal as possible, which usually makes your dog feel better. Also, once kidney disease is advanced, a decreased protein diet will decrease the workload on the kidneys.

  Your veterinarian can recommend a commercially prepared food that has the quantity and quality of protein needed by your dog.

- **A phosphate binder**

  Phosphorous is removed from the body by filtering through the kidneys. Once the filtration process is impaired, phosphorous begins to accumulate in the blood. This also contributes to lethargy and poor appetite. Certain drugs will bind excess phosphates in the intestinal tract so they are not absorbed, resulting in lower blood levels of phosphorus.

- **Fluids given at home**

  Once your dog is stabilized, fluids can be given under the skin (subcutaneously). This serves to continually "restart" the kidneys as their function begins to fail again. This is done once daily to once weekly, depending on the degree of kidney failure.

  Although this might not sound like something you can do, you will be surprised at how easily the technique can be learned and how well most dogs will tolerate it.

- **A drug to regulate the parathyroid gland and calcium levels**

  Calcium and phosphorus must remain at about a 2:1 ratio in the blood. The increase in blood phosphorus level, as mentioned above, stimulates the parathyroid gland to increase the blood calcium level by removing it from bones. This can be helpful for the sake of the normalizing calcium:phosphorus ratio, but it can make the bones brittle and easily broken. Calcitriol can be used to reduce the function of the parathyroid gland and to increase calcium absorption from the intestinal tract. This is recommended if there is evidence of abnormal function of the parathyroid gland.

- **A drug to stimulate the bone marrow to produce new red blood cells**

  The kidneys produce erythropoietin, a hormone that stimulates the bone marrow to make red blood cells. Therefore, many dogs in kidney failure have a low red blood cell count, anemia. Epogen™ or Procrit™, synthetic forms of erythropoietin, will correct the anemia in most dogs. Unfortunately for some dogs, the drug cannot be used long term because the immune system recognizes the drug as "foreign" and will make antibodies (immune proteins) against it. This is recommended if there is persistent anemia present.

How long can I expect my dog to live?

The prognosis is quite variable depending on response to the initial stage of treatment and your ability to perform the follow-up care. However, treatment is encouraged in most situations because many dogs will respond and have a good quality of life for up to 4 years.

LEPTOSPIROSIS

What is leptospirosis?

Leptospirosis is any disease caused by members of the spirochete (coil-shaped) bacterium, *Leptospira interrogans*. There are several variants (serovars) of this bacterium which infect and affect many species of animals world-wide. In dogs the two serovars of importance are *canicola* and *icterohemorrhagiae.*

How do dogs acquire infection?

Leptospira icterohaemorrhagiae is carried mainly by rats and other rodents, but other dogs are the most likely source of *canicola.* Contact with and ingestion of infected urine is the most important means of transmission, but particularly *icterhaemorrhagiae* can penetrate through damaged or soft skin. The incubation period from infection to onset of clinical signs is usually 4 to 12 days.

What are the signs of leptospirosis?

Many infections may go unnoticed, but other cases can be very severe. There are three main forms of disease: hemorrhagic (bleeding), icteric (jaundice) and kidney failure (uremic). In the hemorrhagic disease there is early high fever with lassitude, apathy and total loss of appetite. Multiple small hemorrhages occur in the mouth and conjunctiva. There may be bloody diarrhea and vomiting. Death is quite likely in this form. The jaundice form starts similarly to the hemorrhagic form, and is similar in course apart from the yellowing of mucous membranes. The kidney form is more likely with *Leptospira canicola.* There is a characteristic rancid odor to the breath, and ulceration of the tongue develops. This form may be fatal or become chronic.

How common is leptospirosis?

In recent years, mainly because of widespread vaccination in North America, leptospirosis in dogs has become an uncommon, even rare disease. If vaccination was to be widely discontinued, undoubtedly the infection would rapidly break-out from its wild-life reservoirs.

What is the treatment?

Antibiotics are reasonably effective against leptospira. There is generally a need for intensive medical care including fluid therapy if the animal is to recover. Prevention is much better than having to try to cure?

How can I prevent leptospirosis?

Vaccines have been available for many years and are often included in veterinarians recommendations for routine vaccination with annual boosters. Because of the relative rarity of these infections today, some veterinarians are omitting leptospira vaccines. If this becomes the normal situation, we can expect to see more cases occurring.

Does the vaccine cause reactions?

Of all of the components of a dog's annual boosters, leptospira is the most likely to cause a reaction. This is usually in the form of considerable lethargy or low energy and dogs often stop eating for a couple of days. These reactions are rarely serious but some owners prefer to decline the leptospira vaccine once their dog has experienced this problem.

LICK GRANULOMA

What is a lick granuloma?

A lick granuloma is an open sore on the skin caused and perpetuated by constant licking. The correct medical term for this problem is Acral Lick Dermatitis. It is generally located on one of the legs, usually near the carpus (wrist) joint. Typically, the hair will be licked off and the area will be either raw and weeping or thickened and scarred.

Lick granulomas usually begin with an itching or tingling sensation. The dog responds to this by licking which serves to increase the itching or tingling further. A vicious cycle quickly develops, creating a habit much like a child sucking its thumb. Even if the problem that initiated the itching or tingling sensation is gone, the licking habit continues.

Are there certain breeds that are more likely to do this?

Yes. German Shepherds, Doberman Pinschers, Great Danes, Labrador Retrievers, and Irish Setters develop lick granulomas more often than other breeds, but any breed is susceptible. In addition, male dogs are twice as likely to develop these lesions than females.

Why does a dog do this?

There is no clear answer to this question but there are three basic views on the subject. Some experts consider it to be a primary skin disorder, while others see it as a behavioral problem, or as a neurologic disease involving the nerves in the area of the affected skin. It is likely that most lick granulomas have more than one cause or a single cause with one or more contributing factors.

How is this condition diagnosed and differentiated from other skin disorders?

In most cases, the diagnosis is made based on the appearance and location of the lesion and the observation that the dog has a compulsion to lick the area. However, certain skin tumors, parasites, embedded foreign bodies, and allergies can create lesions that look very similar. In addition, trauma that causes bone fractures or nerve injury can also lead to constant licking, creating a similar lesion. Therefore, if the diagnosis is in doubt or if the dog does not respond well to initial treatment, fungal cultures, radiographs (x-rays), and biopsies may be recommended.

How is a lick granuloma treated?

Many approaches have been attempted, but none have been successful in all cases. Often, success is only achieved after several "trial-and-error" attempts.

The approach to treatment generally begins by trying to eliminate potential psychological factors. Boredom and stress are important issues that should be addressed. It has been suggested that another dog be acquired to keep the affected dog distracted from the licking cycle. Since this approach may not be successful, it should only be considered in situations where you have already thought of acquiring another dog.

If no initiating cause can be found and eliminated, various medications are used. These fall into two categories:

1) drugs which reduce sensation or relieve inflammation or

2) drugs which affect the mood of the dog. In many cases, a drug in each category will be used simultaneously as a means of attacking the problem from two angles.

Some dogs respond best to combination drug therapy and the use of restraint collars. These collars (often called Elizabethan collars because of their appearance) are wide enough to stop the dog reaching the affected area to lick. It may be necessary for the dog to wear the collar for 6 - 8 weeks because skin conditions take a very long time to heal.

Many dogs develop secondary bacterial infections within the lick granuloma so long-term antibiotic therapy (6 - 8 weeks) may be helpful in some cases.

Some alternative treatments have been used which include radiation therapy, surgical excision of the lesion, cryosurgery (freezing), and the injection of cobra antivenom. The success rate is very varied and improvement is reported in 20 - 40% of the cases. These approaches are rather radical and usually employed when other methods fail to be successful.

What is the prognosis?

Lick granuloma is a difficult condition to treat successfully. It is frustrating because the cause is rarely identified and there is a strong psychological component to this condition. Remember that the initial course of treatment may be unsuccessful and that other avenues can be pursued once a lack of response has been observed.

LUMBOSACRAL SYNDROME

What is the lumbosacral syndrome?

This is a disease that occurs at the lumbosacral junction. The term "lumbo" refers to the lumbar vertebrae. These are the bones in the lower part of the spinal column. The term "sacral" refers to the sacrum, which is the part of the spine that joins the lumbar spine and the pelvis. The lumbosacral syndrome is an instability at this strategic point in the spine. This disease is also known as the cauda equina syndrome. This term comes from Latin words that mean "horse's tail." At this level, the spinal cord is no longer a tubular structure. Instead, it is a collection of large nerves that have the appearance of a horse's tail.

What causes it?

Pressure on the cauda equina or the nerves that exit the spine is the mechanism causing the clinical signs. The cause of the pressure may be a narrowed spinal canal, an infection in the disk at this joint, trauma, a spinal tumor, or instability at this joint.

What are the clinical signs?

When instability exists along the spine, abnormal movement occurs. This causes inflammation to the nerves leaving the spinal cord and to the muscles in the immediate area. Affected dogs are in pain and exhibit it in various ways. When pressure is applied to the muscles in the lower back, many dogs will cry or move away. Some dogs may be very slow to rise from a lying position because this movement aggravates the inflamed nerves and muscles. Some will literally fall to their knees when the tail is lifted sharply. Occasionally, dogs develop weakness or lameness in the rear legs with muscle atrophy. Others become fecal or urinary incontinent, and some will mutilate their feet or tail with incessant chewing.

As the problem progresses, the disk that is located between the last lumbar vertebrae and the sacrum may rupture. If this happens, the dog will be uncoordinated when it walks, or it may be paralyzed in the rear legs.

How is it diagnosed?

Radiographs (x-rays) will generally reveal arthritic changes at the lumbosacral junction. However, this is common in many dogs and may not cause any clinical signs. If the disk ruptures, there may be evidence of a narrowed disk space or disk material against the spinal cord. However, these offer only indirect evidence.

If the clinical signs are correct and the initial radiographs are suggestive of the lumbosacral syndrome, a special radiographic study, called an epidurogram, is performed. This is the injection of contrast material around the spinal cord so that pressure on the spinal cord can be detected on subsequent radiographs.

What is the treatment?

If your dog is overweight, weight reduction will be an important part of the treatment. Any disorder of the back is aggravated by excessive body weight.

Strict rest is also an important part of treatment for any back problem. Cage rest is preferable, but confinement in a small fenced run or small room is acceptable.

Anti-inflammatory drugs and pain relievers will often give temporary relief.

Although infection in the disk is not a common cause, it should be treated with appropriate antibiotics if it is present. An infection of this nature usually requires 4 - 8 weeks of therapy.

If the disk ruptures, many dogs will become uncoordinated when they walk, or they may even become paralyzed in the rear legs. If this occurs, surgery is indicated. The surgical procedure, called a dorsal laminectomy, is to relieve the pressure of a bulging or ruptured disk from the spinal cord. It also permits identification of a spinal tumor or a narrowing of the spinal canal due to traumatic injury. Once the pressure is relieved, return of function of the rear legs is expected. However, permanent damage to the spinal cord will not be reversed, and the surgery does not relieve inflammation around the spinal nerves or the muscles. Continued pain relievers or anti-inflammatory drugs may be needed until this aspect of the problem finally resolves.

What is a luxating patella?

The patella, or knee cap, should be located in the center of the knee joint. The term "luxating" means out of place or dislocated. Therefore, a luxating patella is a knee cap that moves out of its normal location.

What causes this to occur?

The muscles of the thigh attach directly or indirectly to the top of the knee cap. There is a ligament, called the patellar ligament, which runs from the bottom of the knee cap to a point on the tibia just below the knee joint (*see* diagram p. 30). When the thigh muscles contract, the force is transmitted through the patella and through the patellar ligament and results in extension (straightening) of the knee joint. The patella stays in the center of the leg because the point of attachment of the patellar ligament is on the midline and because the patella slides in a groove on the lower end of the femur (the bone between the knee and the hip).

The patella luxates because the point of attachment of the patellar ligament is not on the midline of the tibia. It is almost always located too far medial (toward the middle of the body). As the thigh muscles contract, the force is pulled against the groove on the inner side of the femur. After several months or years of this abnormal movement, the inner side of the groove wears down and the patella is free to move out of the groove or dislocate. When this occurs, the dog has difficulty bearing weight on the leg. It may learn how to kick the leg and snap the patella back into its normal location. However, because the side of the groove is gone, it dislocates again easily.

Does a luxating patella cause any long-term problems for my dog?

Some dogs can tolerate this problem for many years, some for all of their lives. However, this weakness predisposes the knee to other injuries, especially torn cruciate ligaments. With advancing age, the joint may become arthritic and painful.

Can a luxating patella be corrected?

Surgery should be performed if your dog has a persistent lameness or if other knee injuries occur secondary to the luxation. Surgical repair is a three step process.

1) The point of attachment of the patellar ligament is cut from the bone and transplanted to its proper location to correct the incorrect alignment.
2) The groove in the femur is deepened so the patella will stay in place.
3) The capsule around the joint is tightened.

This last step is important because the joint capsule will have stretched during the period of luxation. If the surgery is performed before arthritis occurs, the prognosis is excellent. Your dog should regain full use of its leg. However, if arthritis has already occurred, the joint will still be somewhat painful, especially in cold weather.

What is Lyme Disease?

Lyme Disease (not Lyme's Disease) is caused by a spirochete called Borrelia. A spirochete is a type of bacterium. It is transmitted to dogs through the bite of a tick. Once in the blood stream, it is carried to many parts of the body. It is especially likely to localize in joints. It was first thought that only a few types of ticks could transmit this disease, but now it appears that several common species may be involved.

Can this disease also affect people?

Yes, but people do not get it directly from dogs. They get it from being bitten by the same ticks that transmit it to dogs. Therefore, preventing exposure to ticks is important for you and your dog.

How is a dog affected?

Many people having the disease develop a characteristic rash at the site of the bite within 3 to 30 days. For these people, the disease can be easily diagnosed at an early stage. However, symptoms of Lyme Disease are more difficult to detect in animals than in people.

This characteristic rash does not develop in dogs or cats. Because the other symptoms of the disease may be delayed or not recognized, and because the symptoms are similar to those of many other diseases, Lyme Disease in animals is often not considered until other diseases have been eliminated.

Many dogs affected with Lyme Disease are taken to a veterinarian because they seem to be experiencing generalized pain and have stopped eating. Affected dogs have been described as if they were "walking on eggshells." Often these animals have high fevers. Dogs may also become lame because of the disease. This painful lameness often appears suddenly and may shift from one leg to another. If untreated, it may eventually disappear, only to recur weeks or months later.

Some pets are affected with the Lyme Disease organism for over a year before they finally show symptoms. By this time, the disease may be quite widespread in the body.

How is Lyme Disease diagnosed?

Dogs with lameness, swollen joints, and fever are suspected of having Lyme Disease. However, other diseases may also cause these symptoms. There are two blood tests that may be used for confirmation. The first is an antibody test. This test does not detect the actual spirochete in the blood but does detect the presence of antibodies created by exposure to the organism. A test can be falsely negative if the dog is infected but has not yet formed antibodies, or if it never forms enough antibodies to cause a positive reaction. This may occur in animals with suppressed immune systems. Some dogs that have been infected for long periods of time may no longer have enough antibodies present to be detected by the test. Therefore, a positive test is meaningful, but a negative is not.

The second test is the polymerase chain reaction (PCR) test, or DNA testing. This is also known as DNA testing. It is very specific and sensitive. However, not all dogs have the spirochete in their blood cells. If a blood sample is tested, a false negative may occur. The best sample for testing is the fluid from an affected joint.

How is Lyme Disease treated?

Because the Lyme spirochete is a bacterium, it can be controlled by antibiotics. However, a lengthy course of treatment is necessary to completely eradicate the organism. The initial antibiotic selected to treat an infected pet may not be effective against the disease, especially if the infection is long-standing. In this situation, a switch to another antibiotic is often effective. Occasionally, the initial infection will recur, or the pet will become reinfected after being bitten by another infected tick.

How can I prevent my dog from getting Lyme Disease?

The key to prevention is keeping your dog from being exposed to ticks. Ticks are found in grassy, wooded, and sandy areas. They find their way onto an animal by climbing to the top of a leaf, blade of grass, or short tree (especially Cedar trees). Here they wait until their sensors detect a close-by animal on which to crawl or drop. Keeping animals from thick underbrush reduces their exposure to ticks. Dogs should be kept on trails when walked near wooded or tall grass areas.

How do I remove a tick from my dog?

Check your pet immediately after it has been in a tick-infected area. If you find a tick moving on your pet, the tick has not fed. Remove the tick promptly and place it in rubbing alcohol or crush it between two solid surfaces. If you find a tick attached to your pet, grasp the tick with fine tweezers or your finger nails near the dog's skin and firmly pull it straight out. You may need another person to help restrain your dog. Removing the tick quickly is important since the disease is not transmitted until the tick has fed for approximately 12 hours. If you crush the tick, do not get the tick's contents, including blood, on your skin. The spirochete that causes Lyme Disease can pass through a wound or cut in your skin.

Is there a vaccine that will protect my dog from Lyme Disease?

A vaccine is now available for protecting dogs against Lyme Disease. This vaccine is initially given twice, at two week intervals. Annual revaccination is also necessary to maintain immunity. The vaccine has been shown to be safe and very effective.

What is the mitral valve?

The heart has four chambers. The upper chambers are called atria (one chamber is called an atrium), and the lower chambers are called ventricles. The heart is also divided into right and left sides. Blood flows from the body into the right atrium. It is stored there briefly then pumped into the right ventricle. The right ventricle pumps blood into the lungs where it receives oxygen. It flows from the lungs into the left atrium where it is held a few seconds before going into the left ventricle. The left ventricle is surrounded by the largest and strongest of the heart muscles. This large muscle is necessary to pump blood to all parts of the body. Each side of the heart has a valve to keep blood from going backward from the ventricles to the atria. The valve between the left atrium and left ventricle is called the mitral valve. Because of the very large pressure created when the left ventricle contracts, the mitral valve wears out in many dogs. This wearing out process begins with a small leak that gradually gets more severe.

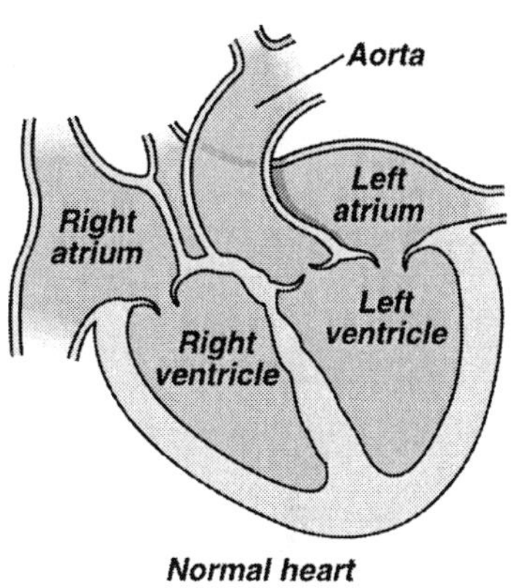

Normal heart

How common is mitral valve disease?

This is the most common cause of heart failure in small dogs. Large breeds have a lower incidence.

What are the consequences of a leaking mitral valve?

The earliest sign of a leaking mitral valve is a heart murmur. This is produced by the turbulence created when some of the blood goes backward through the leaking valve and into the left atrium. Many dogs develop a murmur from the mitral valve as early as 6 years of age. This problem is especially common in small breeds of dogs; most of them will have a murmur by 10 years of age. However, a murmur does not mean that heart failure is imminent. But as time goes on, the leak becomes more severe and more and more blood goes backwards. This results in reduced pumping efficiency and, eventually, congestive heart failure. From the time a murmur develops, it may be a few months to several years until heart failure occurs.

How will I know if heart failure is present?

When the heart is not properly pumping blood, the blood moves more slowly through the lungs. This results in small amounts of fluid leaking out of the capillaries into the air passageways. This fluid collection produces the earliest signs of heart failure. The dog attempts to gag up fluid from the lungs (as if trying to clear the throat), has a chronic, hacking cough, and shows a lack of stamina when exercised.

Does that mean that heart failure will occur soon?

Congestive heart failure begins when the body is not able to provide blood with adequate oxygen for the tissues. Without adequate oxygen, the body's cells become desperate and trigger a series of responses. Various hormones are released in an attempt to correct the problem. These hormones conserve fluid in an effort to increase blood volume and the output of blood and oxygen by the heart. For several months, these compensatory responses help the situation. However, eventually, the increased fluid retention becomes a detriment. More and more fluid leaks out of capillaries causing increased gagging and coughing, reduced stamina, and increased fluid collection in the abdominal cavity and body tissues. Fluid in the lungs is called pulmonary edema, fluid below the skin is called peripheral or limb edema, and fluid in the abdomen is called ascites. When these are present, congestive heart failure is present.

What tests are done to assess the situation?

There are several tests that are used. All provide valuable information while looking at different aspects of heart function.

- **Listening with a stethoscope (auscultation)**

  This valuable tool permits identification of murmurs, their location, and their intensity. It also allows us to hear lung sounds so that we can better understand what is happening within the lungs.

- **Blood and urine tests**

  These do not give direct information about heart function, but they allow detection of other disorders in the body that may have significance to heart function.

- **Chest radiographs (x-rays)**

  The chest radiograph is useful for examining the lungs and for viewing the size and shape of the heart.

- **Electrocardiogram (ECG or EKG)**

  This is an assessment of the electrical activity of the heart. It allows accurate determination of heart rate and rhythm. Arrhythmias (abnormal rhythms) can be detected and evaluated.

- **Ultrasound examination (Sonogram, Echocardiogram)**

  This test uses sound waves that bounce off the structures of the heart and are read on a TV-like monitor. It gives the best look at the size of each heart chamber, and permits visualization of the heart valves. This is seen on the monitor in actual time so the contractions of the heart can be evaluated.

The combination of all of these tests give the best evaluation of the dog and its heart function. However, if cost considerations prohibit performing all of them, two or three will provide much valuable information.

Is there a treatment for a leaky mitral valve and heart failure?

A leaky heart valve can be replaced surgically in people. However, this is usually not feasible in dogs. There are several drugs that will improve heart function, even in the presence of a leaky valve.

- **Diuretics**

  These drugs stimulate the kidneys to remove excess fluid from the body.

- **Nitroglycerin**

  This drug dilates the veins throughout the body, especially the ones going to the heart muscle. This permits better heart contractions and allows blood to move more freely to the other body tissues. However, it is only effective for 1 - 2 days before the body builds tolerance (resistance) to it.

- **Digitalis**

  This drug improves heart function in several ways, including the regulation of excess hormones that have been released, slowing the heart rate, and strengthening each contraction of the heart.

- **Enzyme blockers**

  These are relatively new drugs that can directly block the compensation system that has gotten out of control.

- **Vasodilators**

  These drugs dilate the arteries and veins of the body to permit better blood flow. They may be used long-term because they continue to be effective, as opposed to the short-term effects of nitroglycerin.

Not all of these drugs are used in each dog in heart failure. The results of the various tests will determine which ones are appropriate.

How much longer will my dog live?

There are many factors that must be considered before that question can be answered. The results of the tests are important, and the response that occurs within the first few days is another indicator.

If response does not occur within a few hours to days, the prognosis is not good. However, most dogs that stabilize quickly will live for many months or a few years.

Raising an orphaned puppy is a noble and rewarding experience. The bonding that will occur in the first few days will likely last for many years. However, orphaned puppies are very fragile; raising them requires jumping numerous hurdles. Do not be disappointed if you are not successful.

What problems am I likely to encounter?

Several critical problems must be addressed in caring for orphaned puppies. Among these are chilling, dehydration, and hypoglycemia. These problems are interrelated and may often exist at the same time. Close observation and prompt attention if any of these problems develop are essential to survival. Of course, proper feeding of the orphaned puppy is extremely important.

Chilling

Chilling in newborn puppies can lead to significant mortality. A puppy will dissipate far more body heat per pound of body weight than an adult dog. The normal newborn puppy depends upon radiant heat from its mother to help maintain its body temperature. In the absence of the mother, various methods of providing heat, such as incubators, heat lamps, or hot water bottles can be used. Rectal temperatures in a normal newborn puppy range from 95 - 99°F (35 - 37.2°C) for the first week, 97 - 100°F (36.1 - 37.7°C) for the second and third weeks, and reach the normal temperature of an adult 100 - 102°F; (37.7 - 38.9°C) by the fourth week.

When the rectal temperature drops below 94°F (34.4°C), the accompanying metabolic alterations are life-threatening. Therefore, immediate action is necessary to provide the warmth the puppy needs to survive. A healthy newborn can usually survive chilling if warmed slowly.

During the first four days of its life, the orphaned puppy should be maintained in an environmental temperature of 85 - 90°F (29.4 - 32.2°C). The temperature may gradually be decreased to 80°F (26.7°C) by the seventh to tenth day and to 72°F (22.2°C) by the end of the fourth week. If the litter is large, the temperature need not be as high. As puppies huddle together, their body heat provides additional warmth.

Caution: Too rapid warming of a chilled puppy may result in its death.

Dehydration

The lack of regular liquid intake or the exposure of the puppy to a low humidity environment can easily result in dehydration. The inefficiency of the digestion and metabolism of a chilled puppy may also lead to dehydration and other changes such as those discussed in this paper. Experienced breeders can detect dehydration by the sense of touch. Two signs of dehydration are the loss of elasticity in the skin and dry and sticky mucous membranes (gums) in the mouth. An environmental relative humidity of 55 to 65 percent is adequate to prevent drying of the skin in a normal newborn puppy. However, a relative humidity of 85 to 90 percent is more effective in maintaining puppies if they are small and weak.

Caution: The environmental temperature should not exceed 90°F (32.2°C) when high humidity is provided. A temperature of 95°F (35°C) coupled with relative humidity of 95 percent can lead to respiratory distress.

Hypoglycemia (low blood sugar)

Signs of hypoglycemia (abnormal decrease of sugar in the blood) are severe depression, muscle twitching and sometimes convulsions. If a puppy shows signs of hypoglycemia, a solution containing glucose will have to be administered. A few drops of corn syrup on the tongue can be life-saving.

What do I feed my orphaned puppy?

Total nutrition for the newborn orphans must be supplied by a milk replacer until the puppies are about three weeks of age. At this age, the puppies are ready to start nibbling moistened solid food.

Preferred diets

A commercial puppy milk replacer should be used but for short-term emergencies you can use:

- 1 cup of milk
- 1 tablespoon corn oil
- 1 pinch of salt
- 3 egg yolks (no whites)
- Blend mixture uniformly

Is the temperature of the food important?

Since the newborn may have trouble generating enough heat to maintain its body temperature, the milk replacer should be warmed to 95 - 100°F (35 - 37.8°C) for the best results. The milk replacer should be about the same temperature as the skin on your forearm or slightly warmer. As the puppies grow older, the milk replacer can be fed at room temperature.

How do I feed my puppy?

Spoon feeding is slow and requires great patience. Each spoonful must be slowly "poured" into the puppy's mouth to prevent liquids from entering the lungs. The puppy's head must not be elevated, or the lungs may fill with fluids. Newborn puppies usually do not have a well-developed gag reflex to signal this.

Dropper feeding accomplishes the same result as spoon feeding but is somewhat cleaner and generally speedier.

Baby bottles made for puppies can be used quite successfully in most situations. The size of the hole in the nipple is critical for success. If the bottle is turned upside down and milk replacer drips from the nipple, the hole is too large. Use of this nipple may cause drowning of the puppy. If the bottle is turned upside down and milk replacer comes out only after considerable squeezing of the bottle, the hole is too small. Use of this nipple will result in the puppy becoming discouraged and refusing to nurse. The hole is the proper size if the bottle is turned upside down and milk replacer drips from the nipple with minimal squeezing of the bottle. If you are having trouble enlarging the hole, heat a needle with a match and push it through the nipple several times.

Tube feeding is the easiest, cleanest and most efficient method of hand feeding. However, it requires proper equipment and technique to prevent putting milk replacer into the puppy's lungs. If bottle feeding is not successful, your veterinarian will supply the equipment and demonstrate the proper technique. This is not a difficult procedure, so do not hesitate to ask about it if it is needed.

When and how much do I feed?

Commercial milk replacers have directions on their labels for proper amounts to feed. It is necessary for the puppy's weight to be obtained properly in ounces or grams. The amounts on the labels are based on the puppy getting only the milk replacer. The amounts given are also for a 24 hour period. That quantity should be divided by the number of feedings per 24 hours. Four meals, equally spaced during a 24 hour period, are ample for feeding a puppy when adequate nutrients are provided. Six or more feedings may be necessary if the puppy is small or weak. Hand feeding can generally be ended by the third week and certainly by the fourth. By this time the puppy can consume food, free-choice, from a dish (*see below*).

How do I get the puppy to urinate and defecate?

The puppy's genital area must be stimulated after feeding to cause urination and defecation. The genital area should be massaged with a moist cloth or cotton ball to stimulate action. This cleaning should continue during the first two weeks. If this procedure is not followed, the puppy may become constipated.

When does the puppy start to eat from a bowl?

By three weeks, the puppy can start to eat food from the dish along with the milk replacer. A gruel can be made by thoroughly mixing a puppy food (canned or dry) with the milk replacer to reach the consistency of a thick milk shake. The mixture should not be too thick at first or the puppy will not consume very much. As the consumption of food increases, the amount of milk replacer can be gradually decreased. By four to four and one-half weeks, the orphaned puppy can consume enough moistened solid food to meet its needs. It is better to avoid starting a puppy on a baby food regimen. This creates extra work and can also create a finicky eater. Many such foods will not meet the nutritional needs of a growing puppy.

Should my puppy be treated for worms?

Puppies are routinely treated for worms at 3 and 6 weeks of age. Depending on the parasite load of the puppy and potential re-exposure to parasites, additional dewormings may be recommended. Your veterinarian needs to see the puppy at the appropriate ages so that it can be accurately weighed.

When is the first vaccination given?

The first vaccination is normally given to puppies at 6 - 8 weeks of age. However, if your puppy did not nurse from its mother during the first 2 - 3 days after birth, there will be no protective immunity passed to it. If that is the case, the first vaccination should be given at about 2 - 3 weeks of age.

PANCREATITIS

What is pancreatitis?

The pancreas is a vital organ which lies on the right side of the abdomen. It has two functions: 1) to produce enzymes which help in digestion of food and, 2) to produce hormones, such as insulin. When the pancreas becomes inflamed, the disorder is called pancreatitis. It is a disease process that is seen commonly in the dog. There is no age, sex, or breed predisposition.

There are two main forms of acute (sudden onset) pancreatitis:

1) the mild, edematous form

2) the more severe, hemorrhagic form

A few dogs that recover from an acute episode of pancreatitis may continue to have recurrent bouts of the acute disease, known as chronic, relapsing pancreatitis. The associated inflammation allows digestive enzymes to spill into the abdominal cavity; this may result in secondary damage to surrounding organs, such as the liver, bile ducts, gall bladder, and intestines.

What causes it?

The cause of pancreatitis is not known; however, there may be several contributory factors. It is often associated with a rich, fatty meal. In some cases, it may be associated with the administration of cortisone; however, some dogs with pancreatitis do not have exposure to either.

Under normal conditions, digestive enzymes produced by the pancreas are activated when they reach the small intestines. In pancreatitis, these enzymes are activated prematurely in the pancreas instead of in the small intestines. This results in digestion of the pancreas itself. The clinical signs of pancreatitis are often variable, and the intensity of the disease will depend on the quantity of enzymes that are prematurely activated.

What are the clinical signs?

The diagnosis of pancreatitis is based on three criteria: clinical signs, laboratory tests, and radiographs (x-rays) and/or ultrasound examination. The disease is typically manifested by nausea, vomiting, fever, abdominal pain, and diarrhea. If the attack is severe, acute shock, depression, and death may occur. Laboratory tests usually reveal an elevated white blood cell count; however, an elevated white blood cell count may also be caused by many other things besides pancreatitis. The elevation of pancreatic enzymes in the blood is probably the most helpful criteria in detecting pancreatic disease, but some dogs with pancreatitis will have normal levels. Radiographs and ultrasound studies may show an area of inflammation in the location of the pancreas. Unfortunately, many dogs with pancreatitis will elude detection with any of these tests. Consequently, the diagnosis of pancreatitis may be tentative in some cases.

How is pancreatitis treated?

The successful management of pancreatitis will depend on early diagnosis and prompt medical therapy. The mild form of the disease is best treated by resting the pancreas from its role in digestion. The only way to "turn off" the pancreas is to withhold all oral fluids and food. This approach is accompanied by intravenous fluids to maintain normal fluid and electrolyte balance. In addition, anti-inflammatory drugs are sometimes administered. The presence of shock necessitates the immediate and intense use of intravenous fluids. Antibiotics are also indicated in many cases.

Will my dog recover?

The prognosis depends on the extent of the disease when presented and a favorable response to initial therapy. Dogs that present with shock and depression have a very guarded prognosis. Most of the mild forms of pancreatitis have a good prognosis.

Will there be any long-term problems?

There are three possible long-term complications that may follow severe or repeated pancreatitis. If a significant number of cells that produce digestive enzymes are destroyed, a lack of proper food digestion may follow. This is known as pancreatic insufficiency and can be treated with daily administration of enzyme tablets or powder in the food. If a significant number of cells that produce insulin are destroyed, diabetes mellitus can result and insulin therapy may be needed. In rare cases, adhesions between the abdominal organs may occur as a consequence of pancreatitis. However, most dogs recover with no long-term effects.

PARVOVIRUS INFECTION

What is Canine Parvo?

Canine parvovirus (CPV) infection is a relatively new disease that appeared in 1978. Because of the severity of the disease and its rapid spread through the canine population, CPV has aroused a great deal of public interest. The virus that causes it is very similar to feline distemper, and the two diseases are almost identical. Therefore, it has been speculated that the canine virus is a mutation of the feline virus. However, that has never been proven.

How does a dog become infected with parvovirus?

The causative agent of CPV disease, as the name infers, is a virus. The main source of the virus is the feces of infected dogs. The stool of an infected dog can have a high concentration of viral particles. Susceptible animals become infected by ingesting the virus. Subsequently, the virus is carried to the intestine where it invades the intestinal wall and causes inflammation. Unlike most other viruses, CPV is stable in the environment and is resistant to the effects of heat, detergents, and alcohol. CPV has been recovered from dog feces even after three months at room temperature. Due to its stability, the virus is easily transmitted via the hair or feet of infected dogs, contaminated shoes, clothes, and other objects. Direct contact between dogs is not required to spread the virus. Dogs that become infected with the virus and show clinical signs will usually become ill within 7 - 10 days of the initial infection.

How does this disease affect the dog?

The clinical manifestations of CPV disease are somewhat variable, but generally take the form of severe vomiting and diarrhea. The diarrhea may or may not contain blood. Additionally, affected dogs often exhibit a lack of appetite, depression, and fever. It is important to note that many dogs may not show every clinical sign, but vomiting and diarrhea are the most common signs; vomiting usually begins first. Parvo may affect dogs of all ages, but is most common in dogs less than one year of age. Young puppies less than five months of age are often the most severely affected and the most difficult to treat.

How is it diagnosed?

The clinical signs of CPV infection can mimic other diseases causing vomiting and diarrhea; consequently, the diagnosis of CPV is often a challenge for the veterinarian. The positive confirmation of CPV infection requires the demonstration of the virus in the stool or the detection of anti-CPV antibodies in the blood serum. Occasionally, a dog will have parvovirus but test negative for virus in the stool. Fortunately, this is not a common occurrence. A tentative diagnosis is often based on the presence of a reduced white blood cell count (leukopenia). If further confirmation is needed, stool or blood can be submitted to a veterinary laboratory for the other tests. The absence of a leukopenia does not always mean that the dog cannot have CPV infection. Some dogs that become clinically ill may not necessarily be leukopenic.

Can it be treated successfully?

There is no treatment to kill the virus once it infects the dog. However, the virus does not directly cause death; rather, it causes loss of the lining of the intestinal tract. This results in severe dehydration, electrolyte (sodium and potassium) imbalances, and infection in the bloodstream (septicemia). When the bacteria that normally live in the intestinal tract are able to get into the blood stream, it becomes more likely that the animal will die. The first step in treatment is to correct dehydration and electrolyte imbalances. This requires the administration of intravenous fluids containing electrolytes. Antibiotics and anti-inflammatory drugs are given to prevent or control septicemia. Antispasmodic drugs are used to inhibit the diarrhea and vomiting that perpetuate the problems.

What is the survival rate?

Most dogs with CPV infection recover if aggressive treatment is used and if therapy is begun before severe septicemia and dehydration occur. For reasons not fully understood, some breeds, notably the Rottweiler, have a much higher fatality rate than other breeds.

Can it be prevented?

The best method of protecting your dog against CPV infection is proper vaccination. Puppies receive a parvo vaccination as part of their multiple-agent vaccine given at 8, 12, and 16 weeks of age. In some situations, veterinarians will give the vaccine at two week intervals and an additional booster at 18 to 20 weeks of age. After the initial series of vaccinations when the dog is a puppy, all dogs should be boostered at least once a year. Dogs in high exposure situations (i.e., kennels, dog shows, field trials, etc.) may be better protected with a booster every six months. Pregnant bitches should be boostered within two weeks of whelping in order to transfer protective antibodies to the puppies. The final decision about a proper vaccination schedule should be made by your veterinarian.

Is there a way to kill the virus in the environment?

The stability of the CPV in the environment makes it important to properly disinfect contaminated areas. This is best accomplished by cleaning food bowls, water bowls, and other contaminated items with a solution of 1/2 cup of chlorine bleach in a gallon of water (133 mL in 4 liters of water). It is important that chlorine bleach be used because most "virucidal" disinfectants will not kill the canine parvovirus.

Does parvovirus pose a health risk for me? How about for my cats?

It is important to note that at the present time, there is no evidence to indicate that CPV is transmissible to cats or humans.

PROSTATIC DISEASE

What is the prostate?

The prostate (commonly mispronounced as "prostrate") is a gland located near the neck of the urinary bladder of male dogs. The urethra passes through it shortly after leaving the bladder. The purpose of the prostate is to produce some of the fluids found in normal canine semen.

What are the signs of prostatic disease?

Enlargement of the gland is common with most prostatic diseases. Since the urethra passes through it, enlargement of the prostate compresses the urethra, and urination becomes difficult. Complete urethral obstruction only rarely occurs, but an affected dog will spend quite a bit of time urinating and produces a stream of urine with a small diameter. The colon, located just above the prostate, is sometimes compressed by an enlarged prostate.

This makes defecation difficult. In summary, a dog with prostatic enlargement often has a history of straining to urinate and/or defecate. In addition, some dogs with prostatic disease will have blood in the urine. Bacterial infection of the prostate is sometimes, but not always, involved with production of the bloody urine.

What are the diseases that cause the prostate to enlarge?

There are at least seven diseases affecting the prostate.

- **Benign prostatic hyperplasia**

  This is a non-cancerous enlargement of the gland. It is associated with the hormone testosterone and is the most common disease of the prostate.

- **Squamous metaplasia**

  This is a non-cancerous enlargement of the gland caused by excess amounts of estrogen. An estrogen-producing tumor called a Sertoli cell tumor is usually responsible.

- **Cystic hyperplasia**

  This condition is usually secondary to benign prostatic hyperplasia or squamous metaplasia. It is caused by obstruction of the ducts that carry prostatic secretions to the urethra. Multiple, fluid-filled cavities result.

- **Paraprostatic cysts**

  These are fluid-filled cysts that develop adjacent to the prostate when abnormal tissue remains from embryonic development before the puppy was born. The cysts begin to develop shortly after birth but may not cause problems or be detected until the dog is several years old.

- **Bacterial infection**

  Bacteria may enter and infect the prostate by going up the urethra or by coming down the urethra from an infection in the urinary bladder. It is usually associated with a preexisting abnormality of the prostate, such as benign prostatic hyperplasia.

- **Prostatic abscess**

  This is a progressive form of a bacterial infection. If the ducts that drain the prostate become obstructed, bacteria are trapped in the prostate and form a walled-off site of infection known as an abscess.

- **Prostatic cancer**

  This form is much less common than all of the others. It may be associated with hormones from the testicles, adrenal glands, or pituitary glands or it may occur without any association with hormones.

How are these diagnosed?

The first step in diagnosis is to determine if the prostate is enlarged. This is done by feeling its size either through the abdominal wall or through the rectal wall. It may be confirmed by radiographs (x-rays) or an ultrasound examination.

Because there are so many diseases of the prostate, it is necessary to perform several tests to tell them apart. These tests include cultures of the dog's urine, a microscopic examination of the cells in the urine, and a microscopic examination of the cells in prostatic fluid or in the prostate itself.

Samples of prostatic fluid are recovered by passing a urethral catheter to the level of the prostate and massaging the prostate to "milk" fluid out of it.

Samples of prostatic cells are obtained by aspiration or biopsy via a needle that is either passed through the body wall or passed through the rectal wall. If the prostate is greatly enlarged, it can be aspirated or biopsied through the body wall; otherwise, an approach through the rectal wall is necessary.

An aspiration sample is taken through a very small bore needle and only recovers a few cells. Sometimes this is adequate for analysis; other times it is not.

A needle biopsy sample is obtained through a large bore needle that is passed into the prostate by some form of electronic guidance. This may be with a type of radiograph or with ultrasound. A biopsy sample recovers a piece of tissue that permits a pathologist to make a more accurate diagnosis.

How are they treated?

- Diseases involving primary or secondary bacterial infections are treated with aggressive antibiotic therapy. Because it is difficult to get many antibiotics into the prostate, treatment for several weeks will probably be necessary. Since most of the infections are secondary to another disease, treating the infection is only part of the overall treatment.

- Diseases associated with excessive hormone levels include benign prostatic hyperplasia, cystic metaplasia, and cystic hyperplasia. Since testosterone and estrogen are both formed in the testicles, castration is generally very effective for all of these. The prostate will generally be normal or smaller than normal in size within one month after castration.

- Paraprostatic cysts and prostatic abscesses require major abdominal surgery to drain and remove.

Prostatic cancer does not respond well to any currently used form of treatment. If it is associated with an excess of a hormone, castration may be beneficial; however, most are not and metastasize rather easily to other parts of the body. The prognosis for these is usually poor.

Owning a dog can be an extremely rewarding experience, but it also carries with it quite a bit of responsibility. This chapter will give you the information needed to make some good decisions regarding your puppy.

You should consult regularly with your veterinarian to help you with your puppy's health care. Many problems that could occur later, can be prevented. Prevention is better than cure!

What type of playing should I expect from a puppy?

Stimulating play is important during the first week. Stalking and pouncing are important play behaviors in puppies and are necessary for proper muscular development. If given a sufficient outlet for these behaviors with toys, your puppy will be less likely to use family members for these activities. The best toys are lightweight and movable. These include wads of paper and rubber balls. Any toy that is small enough to be swallowed should be avoided.

Can I discipline a puppy?

Disciplining a young puppy may be necessary if its behavior threatens people or property, but harsh punishment should be avoided. Hand clapping and using shaker cans or horns can be intimidating enough to inhibit undesirable behavior. However, remote punishment is preferred. Remote punishment consists of using something that appears unconnected to the punisher to stop the problem behavior. Examples include using spray bottles, throwing objects in the direction of the puppy to startle (but not hit) it, and making loud noises. Remote punishment is preferred because the puppy associates punishment with the undesirable act and not with you.

When should my puppy be vaccinated?

There are many diseases that are fatal to dogs. Fortunately, we have the ability to prevent many of these by the use of very effective vaccines. In order to be effective, these vaccines must be given as a series of injections. Ideally, they are given at about 6 - 8, 12, and 16 weeks of age, but this schedule may vary somewhat depending on several factors.

The routine vaccination schedule will protect your puppy from seven diseases: distemper (*see* p. 53), hepatitis (*see* p. 78), leptospirosis (*see* p. 97), parainfluenza virus (*see* p. 94), parvovirus (*see* p. 112), coronavirus (*see* p. 29), and rabies (*see* p. 124). The first six are included in one injection that is given at 6 - 8, 12, and 16 weeks old. Rabies vaccine is given at 12 - 16 weeks of age. A final booster for parvovirus is often given at 18 - 20 weeks. There are two other optional vaccinations that are appropriate in certain situations. Your puppy should receive kennel cough vaccine (*see* p. 94) if a trip to a boarding kennel is likely or if it will be placed in a puppy training class. Lyme vaccine is given to dogs that are exposed to ticks because Lyme Disease is transmitted by ticks. Please advise your veterinarian of these needs on your next visit.

Why does my puppy need more than one vaccination?

When the puppy nurses its mother, it receives a temporary form of immunity through its mother's milk. This immunity is in the form of proteins called antibodies. For about 24 - 48 hours after birth, the puppy's intestine allows absorption of these antibodies directly into the blood stream. This immunity is of benefit during the first few weeks of the puppy's life, but, at some point, this immunity fails and the puppy must be able to make its own long-lasting immunity. Vaccinations are used for this purpose. As long as the mother's antibodies are present, vaccinations do not have a chance to stimulate the puppy's immune system. The mother's antibodies interfere by neutralizing the vaccine.

Many factors determine when the puppy will be able to respond to the vaccinations. These include the level of immunity in the mother dog, how much antibody has been absorbed, and the number of vaccines given to the puppy. Since we do not know when an individual puppy will lose the short-term immunity, we give a series of vaccinations. We hope that at least two of these will fall in the window of time when the puppy has lost immunity from its mother but has not yet been exposed to disease. A single vaccination, even if effective, is not likely to stimulate the long-term immunity which is so important. Rabies vaccine is an exception to this, since one injection given at the proper time is enough to produce long-term immunity.

Do all puppies have worms?

Intestinal parasites are common in puppies. Puppies can become infected with parasites before they are born or later through their mother's milk. The microscopic examination of a stool sample will usually help your veterinarian to determine the presence of intestinal parasites. This exam is recommended for all puppies, if a stool sample can be obtained. Even if a stool sample is not possible, the use of a deworming product that is safe and effective against several of the common worms of the dog (*see* Hookworm p. 82, Tapeworms p. 135, Roundworms p. 127, Whipworms p. 146) is recommended. It is important that deworming be repeated in about 3 - 4 weeks, because the deworming medication only kills the adult worms. Within 3 - 4 weeks, the larval stages will have become adults and will need to be treated. Dogs remain susceptible to reinfection with hookworms and roundworms. Periodic deworming throughout the dog's life may be recommended for dogs that go outdoors.

Tapeworms are the most common intestinal parasite of dogs (*see* Tapeworms p. 135). Puppies become infected with them when they swallow fleas; the eggs of the tapeworm live inside the flea. When the puppy chews or licks its skin as a flea bites, the flea may be swallowed. The flea is digested within the dog's intestine; the tapeworm hatches and then anchors itself to the intestinal lining. Therefore, exposure to fleas may result in a new infection; this can occur in as little as two weeks.

Dogs infected with tapeworms will pass small segments of the worms in their stool. The segments are white in color and look like grains of rice. They are about 1/8 inch (3 mm) long and may be seen crawling on the surface of the stool. They may also stick to the hair under the tail. If that occurs, they will dry out, shrink to about half their size, and become golden in color.

Tapeworm segments do not pass every day or in every stool sample; therefore, inspection of several consecutive bowel movements may be needed to find them. A stool sample may be examined at a clinic with negative results and then you may find them the next day. If you find them at any time, please notify your veterinarian so the appropriate drug for treatment can be provided.

How important are heartworms?

Heartworms are important parasites, especially in certain climates (*see* Heartworms p. 72). They can live in your dog's heart and cause major damage to the heart and lungs. Heartworms are transmitted by mosquitoes so your dog does not have to be in contact with another dog to be exposed. Fortunately, we have drugs that will protect your dog from heartworms. These drugs are very safe and very effective if given regularly. One product is a chewable tablet that your dog should eat like a treat; it is given daily. Two others are tablets that are given only once monthly. We recommend the product which is most likely to be given on a regular basis, either daily or monthly. Be aware that having a long haircoat or staying primarily indoors does not protect a dog against heartworm infection.

Heartworm preventatives are dosed according to your dog's weight. As the weight increases, the dosage should also increase. Please note the dosing instructions on the package. These products are very safe. You could overdose your dog by two or three times the recommended dose without causing harm. Therefore, it is always better to overdose rather than underdose.

There are lots of choices of dog foods. What should I feed my puppy?

Diet is extremely important in the growing months of a dog's life, and there are two important criteria that should be met in selecting food for your puppy. Veterinarians usually recommend a **NAME-BRAND FOOD** made by a national dog food company (not a generic or local brand), and a form of food **MADE FOR PUPPIES**. This should be fed until your puppy is about 12 -18 months of age, depending on its size. In the United States it is recommended you only buy food which has the AAFCO certification. Usually, you can find this information very easily on the label. AAFCO is an organization which oversees the entire pet food industry. It does not endorse any particular food, but it will certify that the food has met the minimum requirements for nutrition. Most of the commercial pet foods will have the AAFCO label. Generic brands often do not have it. In Canada, look for foods which are approved by the Canadian Veterinary Medical Association (CVMA).

Feeding a dry, canned, or semi-moist form of dog food is acceptable. Each has advantages and disadvantages. Dry food is definitely the most inexpensive. It can be left in the dog's bowl without drying. The good brands of dry food are just as nutritious as the other forms. As a rule, most veterinarians will recommend dry food for your puppy.

Semi-moist and canned foods are also acceptable. However, both are considerably more expensive than dry food. They often are more appealing to the dog's taste; however, they are not more nutritious. If you feed a very tasty food, you are running the risk of creating a dog with a finicky appetite. In addition, the semi-moist foods are high in sugar.

Table foods are not recommended. Because they are generally very tasty, dogs will often begin to hold out for these and not eat their well-balanced dog food. If you choose to give your puppy table food, be sure that at least 90% of its diet is good quality commercial puppy food.

We enjoy a variety of things to eat in our diet. However, most dogs actually prefer not to change from one food to another unless they are trained to do so by the way you feed them. Do not feel guilty if your dog is happy to just eat one food day after day, week after week.

Commercials for dog food can be very misleading. If you watch carefully you will notice that commercials promote dog food on one basis, TASTE. Nutrition is rarely mentioned. Most of the "gourmet" foods are marketed to appeal to owners who want the best for their dogs; however, they do not offer the dog any nutritional advantage over a good quality dry food, and they are far more expensive. If your dog eats a gourmet food very long, it will probably not be happy with other foods. If it needs a special diet due to a health problem later in life, it is very unlikely to accept it. Therefore, we do not encourage feeding gourmet dog foods.

How do I ensure that my puppy is well socialized?

The socialization period for dogs is between 4 and 12 weeks of age. During that time, the puppy is very impressionable to social influences. If it has good experiences with men, women, children, cats, other dogs, etc., it is likely to accept them throughout life. If the experiences are absent or unpleasant, it may become apprehensive or adverse to any of them. Therefore, during the period of socialization, we encourage you to expose your dog to as many types of social events and influences as possible.

What can be done about fleas on my puppy?

Many of the flea control products that are safe on adult dogs are not safe for puppies less than 4 months of age. Fleas do not stay on your puppy all of their time. Occasionally, they will jump off and seek another host. Therefore, it is important to kill fleas on your new puppy before they can become established in your house. Be sure that any flea product you use is labeled safe for puppies. If you use a flea spray, your puppy should be sprayed lightly. For very young or small puppies, it is safest to spray a cotton ball and use that to wipe the flea spray on the puppy. Flea and tick dip is not recommended for puppies unless they are at least 4 months of age. Remember, not all insecticides that can be used on adult dogs are safe for puppies (*see also* 'Fleas' p. 63).

Can I trim my puppy's sharp toe nails?

Puppies have very sharp toe nails. They can be trimmed with your regular finger nail clippers or with nail trimmers made for dogs and cats. If you take too much off the nail, you will get into the quick; bleeding and pain will occur. If this happens, neither you nor your dog will want to do this again. Therefore, a few points are helpful:

- If your dog has clear or white nails, you can see the pink of the quick through the nail. Avoid the pink area, and you should be out of the quick.

- If your dog has black nails, you will not be able to see the quick so only cut 1/32" (1 mm) of the nail at a time until the dog begins to get sensitive. The sensitivity will usually occur before you are into the blood vessel. With black nails, it is likely that you will get too close on at least one nail.
- If your dog has some clear and some black nails, use the average clear nail as a guide for cutting the black ones.
- When cutting nails, use sharp trimmers. Dull trimmers tend to crush the nail and cause pain even if you are not in the quick.
- You should always have styptic powder available. This is sold in pet stores under several trade names, but it will be labeled for use in trimming nails.

What are ear mites?

Ear mites are tiny parasites that live in the ear canal of dogs (and cats). The most common sign of ear mite infection is scratching of the ears. Sometimes the ears will appear dirty because of a black material in the ear canal; this material is sometimes shaken out. The instrument that is used for examining the ear canals, an otoscope, has the necessary magnification to see the mites. Sometimes, mites are found by taking a small amount of the black material from the ear canal and examining it with a microscope. Although they may leave the ear canals for short periods of time, they spend the vast majority of their lives within the protection of the ear canal. Transmission generally requires direct ear-to-ear contact. Ear mites are common in litters of puppies if their mother has ear mites. Ear infections may also cause the production of a dark discharge in the ear canals. It is important that your puppy be examined to be sure the black material is due to ear mites and not infection. Please do not ask your veterinarian to just dispense medication without having the opportunity to make an accurate diagnosis.

Why should I have my female dog spayed?

Spaying offers several advantages. The female's heat periods result in about 2 - 3 weeks of vaginal bleeding. This can be quite annoying if your dog is kept indoors. Male dogs are attracted from blocks away and, in fact, seem to come out of the woodwork. They seem to go over, around, and through many doors or fences. Your dog will have a heat period about every 6 months. Spaying is the removal of the uterus and the ovaries. Therefore, heat periods no longer occur. In many cases, despite your best effort, the female will become pregnant; spaying prevents unplanned litters of puppies.

It has been proven that as the female dog gets older, there is a significant incidence of breast cancer and uterine infections if she has not been spayed. Spaying before she has any heat periods will virtually eliminate the chance of either. If you do not plan to breed your dog, it is strongly recommended that she be spayed before her first heat period. This can be done anytime after she is 6 months old.

Why should I have my male dog neutered?

Neutering offers several advantages. Male dogs are attracted to a female dog in heat and will climb over or go through fences to find her. Male dogs are more aggressive and more likely to fight, especially with other male dogs. As dogs age, the prostate gland frequently enlarges and causes difficulty urinating and defecating. Neutering will solve, or greatly help, all of these problems that come with owning a male dog. The surgery can be performed any time after the dog is 6 months old.

If I choose to breed my female dog, when should that be done?

If you plan to breed your dog, she should have at least one or two heat periods first. This will allow her to physically mature allowing her to be a better mother without such a physical drain on her. Breeding is not recommended after 5 years of age unless she has been bred prior to that. Having her first litter after 5 years of age increases the risk of problems during the pregnancy and/or delivery. Once your dog has had her last litter, she should be spayed to prevent the reproductive problems older dogs have.

PYOMETRA

What is pyometra?

In its simplest terms, pyometra is an infection in the uterus. However, most cases of pyometra are much more difficult to manage than a routine infection. Infection in the lining of the uterus is established as a result of hormonal changes. Following estrus ("heat"), progesterone levels remain elevated for 8 - 10 weeks and thicken the lining of the uterus in preparation for pregnancy. If pregnancy does not occur for several estrus cycles, the lining continues to increase in thickness until cysts form within it. The thickened, cystic lining secretes fluids that create an ideal environment in which bacteria can grow. Additionally, high progesterone levels inhibit the ability of the muscles in the wall of the uterus to contract.

Are there other situations that cause the changes in the uterus?

Yes. The use of progesterone-based drugs can do this. In addition, estrogen will increase the effects of progesterone on the uterus. Drugs containing both hormones are used to treat certain conditions of the reproductive system.

How do bacteria get into the uterus?

The cervix is the gateway to the uterus. It remains tightly closed except during estrus. When it is open, bacteria that are normally found in the vagina can enter the uterus rather easily. If the uterus is normal, the environment is adverse to bacterial survival; however, when the uterine wall is thickened and cystic, perfect conditions exist for bacterial growth. In addition, when these abnormal conditions exist, the muscles of the uterus cannot contract properly. This means that bacteria that enter the uterus cannot be expelled.

When does it occur?

Pyometra may occur in young to middle-aged dogs; however, it is most common in older dogs. After many years of estrus cycles without pregnancy, the uterine wall undergoes the changes that promote this disease. The typical time for pyometra to occur is about 1 - 2 months following estrus.

What are the clinical signs of a dog with pyometra?

The clinical signs depend on whether or not the cervix is open. If it is open, pus will drain from the uterus through the vagina to the outside. It is often noted on the skin or hair under the tail or on bedding and furniture where the dog has laid. Fever, lethargy, anorexia, and depression may or may not be present. If the cervix is closed, pus that forms is not able to drain to the outside. It collects in the uterus causing distention of the abdomen. The bacteria release toxins which are absorbed into circulation These dogs often become severely ill very rapidly. They are anorectic, very listless, and very depressed. Vomiting or diarrhea may be present. Toxins from the bacteria affect the kidney's ability to retain fluid. Increased urine production occurs, and the dog drinks an excess of water. This occurs in both open- and closed-cervix pyometra.

How is it diagnosed?

A very ill female dog that is drinking an increased amount of water and has not been spayed is always suspected of having pyometra. This is especially true if there is a vaginal discharge or an enlarged abdomen. Dogs with pyometra have a marked elevation of the white blood cell count and often have an elevation of globulins (a type of protein produced by the immune system) in the blood. The specific gravity of the urine is very low due to the toxic effects of the bacteria on the kidneys. However, all of these abnormalities may be present in any dog with a major bacterial infection. If the cervix is closed, radiographs (x-rays) of the abdomen will often identify the enlarged uterus. If the cervix is open, there will often be such minimal uterine enlargement that the radiograph will not be conclusive. An ultrasound examination can also be helpful in identifying an enlarged uterus and differentiating that from a normal pregnancy.

How is it treated?

The preferred treatment is to surgically remove the uterus and ovaries. This is called an ovariohysterectomy ("spay"). However, these dogs are quite ill so the surgery is not as routine as the same surgery in a healthy dog. Intravenous fluids are often needed before and after surgery. Antibiotics are given for 1 - 2 weeks.

My dog is a valuable breeding bitch. Can anything else be done other than surgery?

There is a medical approach to treating pyometra. Progstaglandins are a group of hormones that reduce the blood level of progesterone, relax and open the cervix, and contract the uterus to expel bacteria and pus. They can be used successfully to treat this disease, but they are not always successful and they have some important limitations.

- They cause side-effects of restlessness, panting, vomiting, defecation, salivation, and abdominal pain. The side-effects occur within about 15 minutes of an injection and last for a few hours. They become progressively milder with each successive treatment and may be lessened by walking the dog for about 30 minutes following an injection.

- There is no clinical improvement for about 48 hours so dogs that are severely ill are poor candidates.

- Because they contract the uterus, it is possible for the uterus to rupture and spill infection into the abdominal cavity. This is most likely to happen when the cervix is closed.

There are some important statistics that you should know about this form of treatment:

- The success rate for treating open-cervix pyometra is 75 - 90%.
- The success rate for treating closed-cervix pyometra is 25 - 40%.
- The rate of recurrence of the disease is 50 - 75%.
- The chances of subsequent successful breeding is 50 - 75%.

What happens if neither of the above treatments are given?

The chance of successful treatment without surgery or prostaglandin treatment is extremely low. If treatment is not performed quickly, the toxic effects from the bacteria will be fatal. If the cervix is closed, it is also possible for the uterus to rupture, spilling the infection into the abdominal cavity. This will also be fatal.

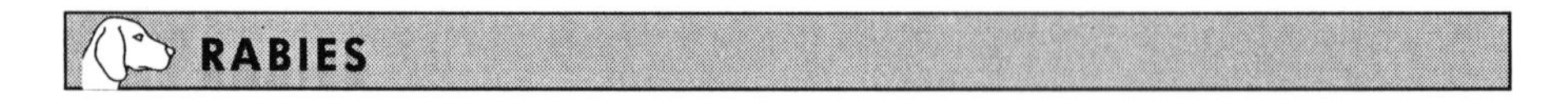

RABIES

What is rabies?

Rabies is a virus disease which is characterized by severe neurological disturbance. It can affect any warm-blooded species of animal, including of course, people, and is almost always fatal.

What are the signs?

Three stages of the disease are recognized. An early 'prodromal' phase where there may be a marked change in temperament. The quiet dog becomes agitated; the active dog becomes nervous, shy. Pupils of the eyes may be dilated, the animal salivates excessively, may snap at the air. After 2 or 3 days the 'excitative' phase takes over. There is exaggerated response to any stimuli. Bizarre changes in appetite lead to swallowing sticks, stones or other objects. The animal may roam aimlessly, inflict self-trauma, have a change in vocalization. There will often be vicious, aggressive behavior, even towards the owner. Seizures may occur. Sometimes there is a 'dumb' form of rabies where the animal is extremely depressed, the mouth may gape open with the tongue protruding. A progressive paralysis may occur.

Are there diseases which can be mistaken for rabies?

There are a number of conditions which can cause some of the signs of rabies. A few conditions can be very similar. Confirmation can only be made by laboratory tests, usually post mortem.

How can I catch rabies?

Rabies is very seldom transmitted except by the bite of a rabid animal. Even then the virus is present in the saliva of the infected animal for a limited time. However if you are bitten by any animal that you do not know the rabies vaccination status of, you should immediately wash the wound thoroughly with soap and water. Try and establish who the owner of the animal is, and whether they are fully vaccinated for rabies. In any case seek medical opinion. Post-exposure rabies treatment with serum and/or vaccine may be recommended. This is very successful when commenced promptly.

Should I get my dog vaccinated?

Rabies vaccines are very safe and very effective. Therefore it is recommended for any dog other than those that live a totally in-door existence. Vaccination for rabies is usually done at three to four months of age, and then every one to three years (depending on vaccine and relative risk which your veterinarian will advise).

RINGWORM

What is ringworm, and what causes it?

Ringworm is a skin disease caused by a fungus. Because the lesions are often circular, it was once thought to be caused by a worm curling up in the tissue. However, the condition has nothing to do with a worm. There are four fungal species affecting dogs which can cause the disease that we call ringworm. These may also affect humans. The fungi live in hair follicles and cause the hair shafts to break off at the skin line. This usually results in round patches of hair loss. As the fungus multiplies, the lesions may become irregularly shaped and spread over the dog's body.

How long does it take to get it?

The incubation period is 10 - 12 days. This means that following exposure to the fungus, about 10 - 12 days will pass before any lesions occur.

How is ringworm diagnosed?

Diagnosis is made in one of 3 ways:

- Identification of the typical "ringworm" lesions on the skin.
- Fluorescence of infected hairs under a special light (however, only 2 of the 4 species of fungi fluoresce).
- Culture of the hair for the fungus. The last method is the most accute, but it may take up to 2 - 3 weeks for the culture to become positive.

How is it transmitted?

Transmission occurs by direct contact between infected and non-infected individuals. It may be passed from dogs to cats and visa versa. It may also be passed from dogs or cats to people and visa versa. If your child has ringworm, he or she may have gotten it from your pet or from another child at school. Adult humans usually are resistant to infection unless there is a break in the skin (a scratch, etc.), but children are quite susceptible. If you or your family members have suspicious skin lesions, check with your family physician. Transmission may also occur from the infected environment. The fungal spores may live in bedding or carpet for several months. They may be killed with a dilution of chlorine bleach and water (1 pint of chlorine bleach in a gallon of water) (500 mL in 4 liters) where it is feasible to use it.

How is it treated?

There are several means of treatment. The specific method(s) chosen for your dog will depend on the severity of the infection, how many pets are involved, if there are children in the household, and how difficult it will be to disinfect your pets' environment.

- **Griseofulvin**

  This is a drug that is concentrated deep in the hair follicles where it can reach the site of active fungal growth. Griseofulvin should be given daily. Dogs with active lesions should receive the tablets for a minimum of 30 days. At that time, your dog should be rechecked to be sure the infection is adequately treated. These tablets are not absorbed from the stomach unless there is fat in the stomach at the time they are given. This can be accomplished by feeding a high fat diet, such as a rich canned dog food or a small amount of fat trimmings from meats (often available at the meat departments of local grocery stores upon request of the butcher) or by allowing the dog to drink some rich cream. This is the most important part of the treatment. If you are not successful in giving the tablets, please call your veterinarian for help. If you are aware of fat consumption having caused a problem for your dog in the past or if your dog has had an episode of pancreatitis, bring this to your veterinarians attention immediately.

- **Topical antifungal medication**

  Apply one of these products to the affected areas once daily for 10 days. Do not risk getting it in your dog's eyes by treating lesions very near the eye.

- **Baths using an antifungal shampoo**

  A bath should be given 3 times on an every other day schedule. Bathe exposed but unaffected pets once. These baths are important in getting the spores off the hairs so they do not drop into the environment and result in re-exposure. A lather should be formed and left on for 5 minutes before rinsing.

- **Lime Sulfur Dip**

  This should be done twice weekly for the first two weeks then once weekly for 4 - 6 weeks. Lime sulfur dip should also be applied to other pets (dogs or cats) in the household to prevent them from being affected. If they develop ringworm lesions, they should begin on griseofulvin. You should wear latex or rubber gloves when applying the dip. This is an effective form of treatment, but the dip has an objectionable odor and can tarnish jewelry.

- **Shaving of the dog's hair**

  This will remove the infected hair. This is recommended only when the infection is extensive.

What should I expect from treatment?

Treatment will not produce immediate results. The areas of hair loss will get larger before they begin to get smaller. Within 1 - 2 weeks, the hair loss should stop, there should be no new areas of hair loss, and the crusty appearance of the skin should subside and the skin look more normal. If any of these do not occur within two weeks, your dog should be checked again.

How long will my dog be contagious?

Infected pets remain contagious for about 3 weeks if aggressive treatment is used. Contagion will last longer if only minimal measures are taken of if you are not faithful with the prescribed approach. Minimizing exposure to other dogs or cats and to your family members is recommended during this period.

I have heard that some dogs are never cured. Is this true?

When treatment is completed, ringworm should be cured. A carrier state can exist, usually because treatment is not long or aggressive enough or because there is some underlying disease compromising the immune system.

ROUNDWORM INFECTION

What are roundworms?

As their name implies, these are worms which have round bodies. On average, they are about 3 - 5 inches (7 - 12 cm) long. They live in the dog's intestines and consume partially digested food. Unlike hookworms, they do not attach to the intestinal wall; rather, they literally swim in their food. Roundworms, sometimes called ascarids, pass moderate numbers of microscopic eggs which are found in the dog's stool. Like hookworm eggs, they must be found with a microscope.

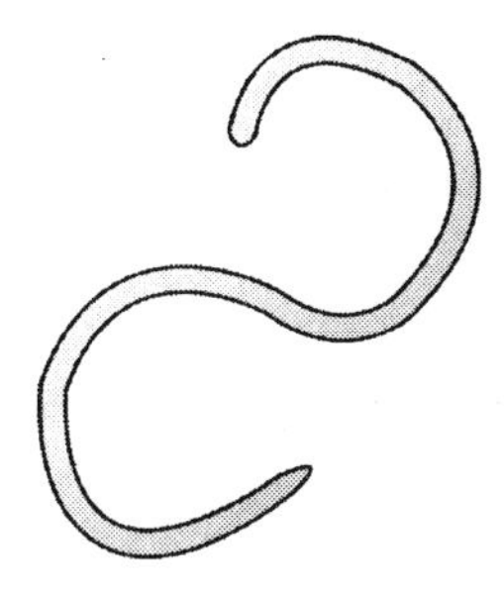

Roundworm (actual size)

How did my dog get roundworms?

Puppies born to mothers that have had roundworms at any time in the past can transmit them to their puppies before birth. This is true even if the mother tests negative for roundworms because roundworm larvae (immature worms) encyst in the mother's muscle tissue and are not detected by our tests for adult worms. Another major source of roundworm infection for puppies is the mother's milk. Roundworm larvae may be present in the mother's mammary glands and milk throughout the period of nursing the puppies. Both puppies and adult dogs may become infected by swallowing roundworm eggs which contain infective larvae. The larvae hatch out in the dog's stomach and small intestine and migrate through the muscle, liver, and lungs. After several weeks, the larvae make their way back to the intestine to mature. When these worms begin to reproduce, new eggs will pass in the dog's stool, and the life cycle of the parasite is completed. Obviously, roundworm eggs passed in one dog's stool may be infectious to other dogs. Interestingly, a large number of other animal species have been found to harbor roundworms and represent potential sources of infection for dogs. These include cockroaches, earthworms, chickens, and rodents.

What kinds of problems do roundworms cause for my dog?

They are not highly pathogenic (harmful) to adult dogs, but large numbers can cause weight loss and a pot-bellied appearance to puppies and weakness in adults. Decreased appetite, vomiting or diarrhea will be observed on occasion. Puppies will sometimes die with serious roundworm infections.

How is roundworm infection diagnosed?

Roundworms are diagnosed by a microscopic examination of the dog's stool. They pass only a moderate number of eggs, so examination of more than one stool sample may be necessary to find them. Occasionally, the mature worms can be found in the dog's stool or vomit.

How are roundworms treated?

Treatment is quite simple. Several very safe and effective drugs are available to kill roundworms in the intestine. Some of these drugs temporarily anesthetize the worms so that they pass out of the dog with a normal bowel movement. The live or dead worms are found in the stool. Because of their large size, they are easily seen. At least two or three treatments are needed; they are typically performed at 2 - 4 week intervals. None of these treatments will kill the immature forms of the worm or the migrating larvae.

The eggs are highly resistant to most commonly used disinfectants and to even harsh environmental conditions. Therefore, removal of the dog's stool is the most effective means of preventing reinfection. A 1% solution of household bleach can be used to remove the sticky outer coating of the eggs, making it easier to rinse them away. This does not, however, kill the eggs. Remember the obvious limitations about where bleach may be safely applied.

Are canine roundworms infectious to people?

Yes. The roundworms of both dogs and cats pose a health risk for humans. As many as 10,000 cases of roundworm infection in humans have been reported in one year. Children, in particular, are at risk for health problems should they become infected. A variety of organs may be affected as the larvae migrate through the body. In suitable environments, the eggs may remain infective to humans (and to dogs) for *years*.

What can be done to control roundworm infection in dogs and to prevent human infection?

- Pregnant bitches should be dewormed in late pregnancy to reduce potential contamination of the environment for newborn puppies.
- All new puppies should be treated by 2 - 3 weeks of age. To effectively break the roundworm life cycle, puppies should be dewormed on the schedule recommended by your veterinarian.
- Prompt deworming should be given when any parasites are detected; periodic deworming may be appropriate for dogs at high risk for reinfection. Adult dogs remain susceptible to reinfection with roundworms throughout their lives.
- Dogs with predatory habits should have a fecal examination several times a year. Rodent control is desirable since rodents may serve as a source of roundworm infection for dogs.
- Prompt disposal of all dog feces is important, especially in yards, playgrounds, and public parks.
- Strict hygiene is especially important for children. Do not allow children to play in potentially contaminated environments.
- Most heartworm prevention products contain a drug that will prevent roundworm infections. However, these products will not kill the adult roundworms so they must be treated if present.

SARCOPTIC MANGE

What is sarcoptic mange?

Mange is a parasitic skin disease caused by microscopic mites. Two different mange mites cause skin disease in dogs. One lives just under the surface of the skin, while the other resides deep in the hair follicles. Although both mites share some similar characteristics, there are also important differences. It is important not to confuse the two types of mange because they have different causes, treatments, and prognoses.

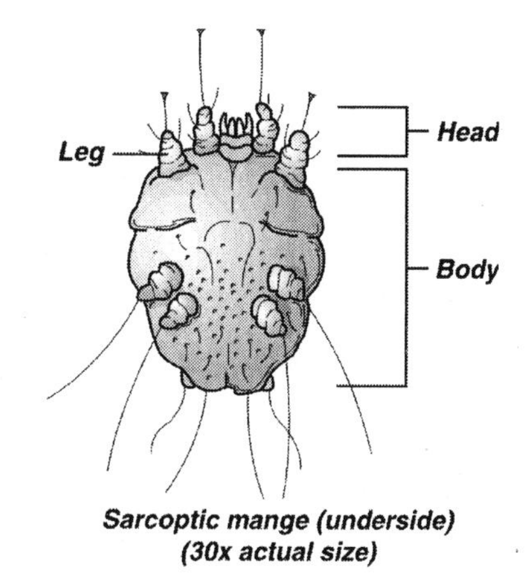

Sarcoptic mange (underside)
(30x actual size)

What causes sarcoptic mange?

Sarcoptic mange is caused by a mite that burrows just beneath the surface of the skin. It may also crawl around on the skin surface. This mite feeds on material in and on the skin.

What does it do to the dog?

The presence of the sarcoptic mite causes severe itching. The dog will chew and scratch its skin constantly. This leads to the loss of large amounts of hair, especially on the legs and belly. Eventually, the skin will become thickened and will darken due to pigmentation.

Is it contagious?

Sarcoptic mange is highly contagious to other dogs; it is also contagious to humans. The dog's bedding should be washed in hot water with bleach or, preferably, discarded. Although the mites are not able to complete their life cycle on humans, they will cause quite a bit of itching before they finally die.

How is sarcopitc mange diagnosed?

Diagnosis is made by a skin scraping that is examined under the microscope. However, only a small number of mites may be present. Because of this, a dog may be strongly suspected of having sarcoptic mange, but all skin scrapings are negative. A presumptive diagnosis can be made because the signs are quite typical. Age is not a significant factor in sarcoptic mange. Although most common in puppies, it affects dogs of all ages.

How is it treated?

There are several insecticides which are effective against this mite. Various dips have been used successfully. Dipping should occur weekly for at least 4 weeks, at which time your dog should be re-examined to determine if further treatment is needed.

Instructions

- Bathe your dog in any good pet shampoo then slowly pour the diluted dip over your dog(s). This should be done on a weekly basis for 4 weeks. Carefully read the dilution instructions on the bottle. Do not rinse off the dip; air drying is preferred. A towel or hair dryer may be used, especially if the temperature is cool.
- Your dog's bedding should be washed in hot water with bleach or discarded.
- If relief from itching does not begin within 5 days after treatment begins, you should call your veterinarian.
- Contact your physician if any family members develop an itching skin rash. Tell your physician that you have been exposed to sarcoptic mange (also known as scabies). In people, the mite cannot complete its life cycle so it will die in a few days. However, it may cause itching during that time. Reinfestation from the dog or the premises can result in continued itching.

SEIZURES

What is a seizure?

Seizures are one of the most frequently seen neurological problems in dogs. A seizure is also known as a convulsion or fit. It may have all or any combination of the following:

- Loss or derangement of consciousness
- Contractions of all the muscles in the body
- Changes in mental awareness from non-responsiveness to hallucinations
- Involuntary urination, defecation, or salivation
- Behavioral changes, including non-recognition of owner, viciousness, pacing, and running in circles

What are the three phases of a seizure?

Seizures consist of three components:

- **Pre-ictal phase**

  The pre-ictal phase, or aura, is a period of altered behavior in which the dog may hide, appear nervous, or seek out the owner. It may be restless, nervous, whining, shaking, or salivating. This may last a few seconds to a few hours.

- **Ictal phase**

  The ictal phase is the seizure itself and lasts from a few seconds to about 5 minutes. During this period, all of the muscles of the body contract strongly. The dog usually falls on its side and seems paralyzed while shaking. The head will be drawn backward. Urination, defecation, and salivation often occur. If it is not over within 5 minutes, the dog is said to be in status epilepticus or prolonged seizure.

- **Post-ictal**

  During the post-ictal phase, there is confusion, disorientation, salivation, pacing, restlessness, and/or temporary blindness. There is no direct correlation between the severity of the seizure and the duration of this phase.

Is the dog in trouble during a seizure?

Despite the dramatic signs of a seizure, the dog feels no pain, only bewilderment. Dogs do not swallow their tongues. If you put your fingers into its mouth, you will do no benefit to your pet and will run a high risk of being bitten very badly. The important thing is to keep the dog from falling and hurting itself. As long as it is on the floor or ground, there is little chance of harm occurring. If seizures continue for longer than a few minutes, the body temperature begins to rise. If hyperthermia develops secondary to a seizure, another set of problems may have to be addressed.

What causes seizures?

There are many, many causes of seizures. Epilepsy is the most common and of least consequence to the dog. The other extreme includes severe diseases such as brain tumors. Fortunately, most are due to epilepsy.

Now that the seizure is over, can anything be done to understand why it happened?

When a seizure occurs, a thorough history concentrating on possible exposure to poisonous or hallucinogenic substances or history of head trauma is taken. A physical examination, a basic battery of blood tests, and an electrocardiogram (EKG) is also performed. These tests rule out disorders of the liver, kidneys, heart, electrolytes, and blood sugar level. A heartworm test is performed if your dog is not taking heartworm preventative very regularly.

If these tests are normal and there is no exposure to poison or recent trauma, further diagnostics may be performed depending on the severity and frequency of the seizures. Occasional seizures are of less concern than when the seizures are becoming more severe and frequent. In this instance, a spinal fluid tap and fluid analysis may be performed. Depending on availability, specialized imaging of the head with a CAT scan or MRI might be performed. Fortunately, these additional tests are usually not needed.

What can be done to prevent future seizures?

Veterinarians generally prescribe 1 - 2 weeks of anticonvulsant therapy. If there are no more seizures during that time, the anticonvulsants are gradually discontinued. The next treatment is determined by how long it takes for another seizure to occur. That may be days, months, or years. At some point, many dogs have seizures frequently enough to justify continuous anticonvulsant therapy. Since that means that medication must be given every 12 to 24 hours for the rest of the dog's life, that is not recommended until seizures occur about every 30 days or unless they last more than 5 minutes.

It is important to avoid sudden discontinuation of any anticonvulsant medication. Even *normal* dogs may be induced to seizure if placed on anticonvulsant medication and then abruptly withdrawn from it. Your veterinarian can outline a schedule for discontinuing the medication.

You mentioned status epilepticus. What does that mean?

Status epilepticus bears special note. It is characterized by a seizure that lasts more than 5 minutes. When it occurs, the dog's life is endangered. Unless intravenous medication is given promptly, the patient may die. If this occurs, you should seek treatment by a veterinarian immediately.

What is Staph?

Staph is a commonly used abbreviation for *Staphylococcus*, a group of bacteria commonly found on the skin. Dermatitis is a term that means that the skin is inflamed.

Does Staph always cause dermatitis?

No. In fact, *Staph* is a normal resident of the skin of animals and humans; however, it is considered an opportunist. As long as the skin is healthy, *Staph* is dormant. But once the skin is irritated, *Staph* can invade the area and multiply rapidly.

What are likely causes of this type of skin irritation?

Scratching is the most common cause. Any disorder that causes itching can create the situation which allows *Staph* to become a problem. Common causes of itching include fleas, inhalant allergy, and food allergy. Irritating chemicals, such as flea and tick dips, also can cause itching.

How is Staph dermatitis diagnosed?

There are two typical *Staph* lesions. One type begins as a red area on the skin with a pimple-like pustule in the center. The other type is a circular, reddish area with a crusty edge and hair loss in the center. The latter can easily be confused with ringworm. Finding either of these skin patterns in a dog that is scratching is highly suggestive of *Staph*.

Confirmation can be made with cultures or skin biopsy. However, the lesions are so typical that this is usually not necessary.

How is Staph dermatitis treated?

This bacterium is usually sensitive to several antibiotics. These include erythromycin, enrofloxicin, amoxicillin with clavulanic acid, lincomycin, dicloxacillin, and oxacillin. Since these medications can be given orally, treatment can occur at home. However, some infections may require 3 - 6 weeks of treatment before the infection is under control. Antibacterial shampoos and ointments can also be helpful in bringing about rapid control of the infection.

The other essential part of treatment is stopping itching and scratching. Other tests may be needed to determine the cause or causes. Frequently, more than one condition contributes to itching.

Is my dog contagious to me or other pets?

No. All dogs, cats, and people have *Staph* living on the skin as a normal resident.

I finished treatment for Staph dermatitis two weeks ago, and now the Staph infection is back. Why is that?

This situation may be caused by an allergy to the *Staph* bacteria. This is called *Staph* hypersensitivity or *Staph* allergy.

The skin lesions that are caused by this disease are identical to those of a *Staph* dermatitis. The difference is recurrence. If *Staph* dermatitis is treated properly, the underlying cause is eliminated and itching is stopped, then the bacterial skin disease should be eliminated. This situation may recur if itching returns. However, when the dog with *Staph* hypersensitivity is treated, the skin lesions will return within a few days or weeks.

Since differentiation of *Staph* dermatitis and *Staph* hypersensitivity is based largely on recurrence, it is very important that treatment be continued long enough. This often means a month or more of antibiotics. If not, there will still be a question of which disease is present.

How is Staph hypersensitivity treated?

Treatment begins the same as for *Staph* dermatitis: oral antibiotics, medicated shampooing, and whatever is necessary to stop the itching. However, long-term control is best achieved with *Staph* bacterin.

Staph bacterin is a solution of killed *Staph* bacteria that is injected into the dog in very tiny amounts. This is an attempt to reprogram the dog's immune system so it does not over-react to its own bacteria.

The use of *Staph* bacterin begins as a series of daily injections into the layers of the skin. After the initial series is completed, the injections are given subcutaneously (just below the skin) on an interval of every 3 - 4 days to every 2 weeks. Since this is an ongoing treatment, it is done by you at home.

I have never given injections so I don't think that I can do this.

It is much easier than you think. Most people can be taught to give the injections in just a few minutes. Don't decide that you cannot do this until your veterinarian shows you the technique.

How successful is this?

Allergy shots are never successful 100% of the time, whether in dogs or in people. Up to 75% of the dogs treated are expected to respond well.

What happens if Staph bacterin is not successful?

If your dog does not respond, it will have to be treated periodically with oral antibiotics and medicated baths. This is not the most desirable approach because *Staph* will often develop resistance to the antibiotics. If this occurs, a change in the specific antibiotic used will be necessary.

TAPEWORM INFECTION

What are tapeworms?

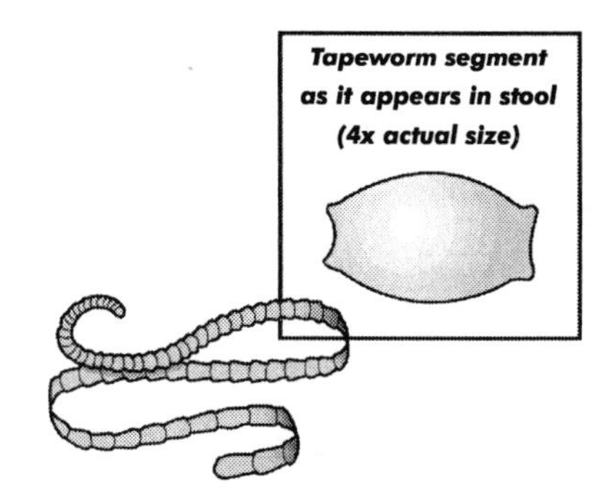

Tapeworm (half actual size)

The most common tapeworm of dogs (and cats) is called *Dipylidium caninum*. This parasite attaches to the small intestinal wall by hook-like mouthparts. Adult tapeworms may reach 8 inches (20 cm) in length. The adult worm is actually made up of many small segments about 1/8 inch (3 mm) long. As the tail end of the worm matures, the terminal segments break off and pass into the stool. Occasionally, the mobile segments can be seen crawling near the anus or on the surface of a fresh bowel movement. These segments look like grains of rice and contain tapeworm eggs; the eggs are released into the environment when the segment dries. The dried segments are small (about 1/16", or 2 mm), hard and golden in color. These dried segments can sometimes be seen stuck to the hair around the dog's anus.

How did my dog get tapeworms?

First, tapeworm eggs must be swallowed by flea larvae (an immature stage of the flea). Contact between flea larvae and tapeworm eggs is thought to occur most frequently in contaminated bedding or carpet. The life cycle of the tapeworm cannot be completed unless the flea swallows tapeworm larvae.

Next, the dog chews or licks its skin as a flea bites; the flea is then swallowed. As the flea is digested within the dog's intestine, the tapeworm hatches and anchors itself to the intestinal lining.

What kind of problems do tapeworms cause for the dog?

Tapeworms are not highly pathogenic (harmful) to your dog. They may cause debilitation and weight loss when they occur in large numbers. Sometimes, the dog will scoot or drag its anus across the ground or carpet because the segments are irritating to the skin in this area. The adult worm is generally not seen, but the white segments which break away from the tapeworm and pass outside the body rarely fail to get an owner's attention! Occasionally, a tapeworm will release its attachment in the intestines and move into the stomach. This irritates the stomach, causing the dog to vomit the worm. When this happens, a worm several inches in length will be seen.

How is tapeworm infection diagnosed?

Tapeworm infection is usually diagnosed when the white, mobile segments are seen crawling on your dog or in the stool. Tapeworms are not usually detected by the routine fecal examination performed by the veterinarian. Because of this, veterinarians depend on the owner to notify them of possible tapeworm infection in the dog.

How is tapeworm infestation treated?

Treatment is simple and, fortunately, very effective. A drug which kills tapeworms is given, either orally or by injection. It causes the tapeworm to dissolve within the intestines. Since the worm is usually digested before it passes, it is not visible in your dog's stool. These drugs should not cause vomiting, diarrhea, or any other adverse side-effects. Control of fleas is very important in the management and prevention of tapeworm infection. Flea control involves treatment of your dog, the indoor environment and the outdoor environment where the dog resides. If the dog lives in a flea-infested environment, reinfection with tapeworms may occur in as little as two weeks. Because the medication which treats tapeworm infection is so effective, return of the tapeworms is almost always due to reinfection from the environment.

How do I tell tapeworms from pinworms?

Tapeworms and pinworms look very similar. However, contrary to popular belief, pinworms do not infect dogs or cats. Any worm segments seen associated with dogs are due to tapeworms. Children who get pinworms do not get them from dogs or cats.

Are canine tapeworms infectious to people?

Yes, although infection is not common or likely. A flea must be ingested for humans to become infected with the most common tapeworm of dogs. Most reported cases have involved children. The most effective way to prevent human infection is through aggressive, thorough flea control. The risk of infection with this tapeworm in humans is quite small but does exist.

One less common group of tapeworms, called *Echinococcus*, is of particular concern as a threat to human health. These tapeworms cause very serious disease when humans become infected. This parasite is harder to diagnose than the tapeworm caused by fleas because the segments are small and not readily seen. Hunters and trappers in the north central United States and south central Canada may be at risk for infection by this worm if strict hygiene is not observed. Foxes and coyotes (and the wild rodents upon which they prey) are important in the life cycle of this parasite. Dogs and cats may also become infected if they eat rodents carrying the parasite. When eggs of *Echinococcus* are passed in the feces of the dog and cat, humans are at risk for infection. Free-roaming cats and dogs may need to be periodically treated with tapeworm medication. Rodent control and good hygiene are important in preventing the spread of this disease to humans. As with the more common tapeworm, infection with *Echinococcus* is infrequent but possible.

What can be done to control tapeworm infection in dogs and to prevent human infection?

- Effective flea control is important.
- Prompt deworming should be given when parasites are detected; periodic deworming may be appropriate for pets at high risk for reinfection.
- All pet feces should be disposed of promptly, especially in yards, playgrounds, and public parks.
- Strict hygiene is important, especially for children. Do not allow children to play in potentially contaminated environments.

How does tartar form, and what does it do?

Plaque is a gummy substance that forms on the teeth within a few hours after a meal. Within 24 hours, plaque starts to harden into tartar. Tartar is harmful in two ways. First, it serves as a place where bacteria can reside and multiply in the mouth. There is substantial scientific evidence that bacteria from tartar get into the blood stream and are deposited in various organs. Heart and kidney disease may result. Second, tartar builds up at the gum line. As the tartar deposit gets larger, it pushes the gums away from the roots of the teeth. Eventually, the teeth will loosen and fall out.

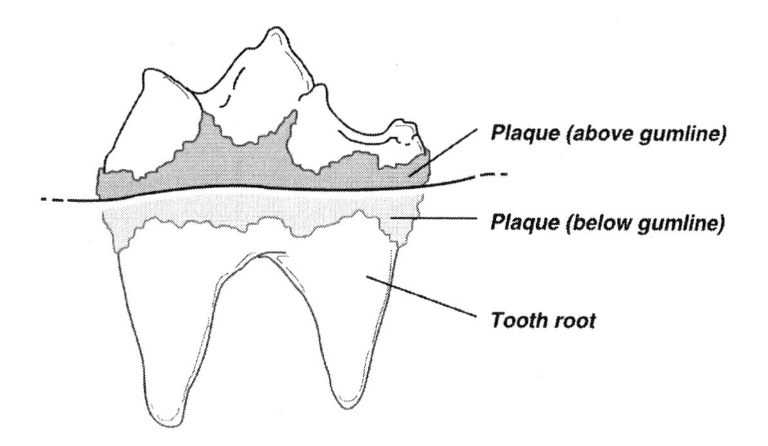

Molar Tooth with Dental Plaque

How can I prevent tartar formation on my dog's teeth?

After your dog's teeth have been cleaned, the following steps are recommended which will help to reduce the process of plaque and tartar buildup.

- Brushing of the teeth is the most effective means of removing plaque before it turns into tartar. We recommend the use of a toothpaste made especially for dogs. This needs to be done at least twice weekly (preferably daily), but we know that not all dogs will tolerate it. Special brushes are made that make this task easier.

- Feed your dog Prescription Diet t/d™. This is a food that has been shown to greatly reduce tartar buildup. It is formulated as a dry food and is composed of large pieces. Because the pieces are too large to be swallowed whole, your dog must chew them. The food contains fibers that literally scrape the plaque off of the teeth without damaging the enamel. By removing plaque as it forms, tartar formation is greatly diminished.

- Use a "mouthwash" that is added to your dog's drinking water or placed in the mouth. This type of product reduces the bacterial count in the mouth, resulting in improved breath.

- Cleaning the teeth every 6 - 12 months or at the first sign of tartar buildup can be very beneficial to most dogs. This will minimize damage to the gums and roots.

Encouraging chewing of raw-hide or dental chew toys. Dogs which chew more tend to accumulate tartar more slowly.

TONSILLITIS

I know that children have tonsillitis, but I did not realize that dogs do. Is it common?

Since dogs have tonsils, they also have tonsillitis. It is quite common in small breeds of dogs and much less common in large dogs.

What are the tonsils, and what do they do?

The tonsils are much like lymph nodes (lymph glands). There are two of them, and they are located in the back of the throat. When they are normal, they are not easily seen because they reside in crypts (pouches). Like lymph nodes, their job is to fight infection. When they are doing this, they often become infected themselves and will enlarge. Swollen, red tonsils that are out of their crypts are easily seen in the back of the throat if the dog will permit its mouth to be opened widely.

How did my dog get tonsillitis?

There are certain conditions known to cause tonsillitis. Chronic vomiting, a chronic productive cough, and chronic disease in the mouth will allow bacteria to infect the tonsils. The main cause of chronic disease in the mouth is tartar on the teeth and the infections that are associated with it. Occasionally, primary tonsillitis (no underlying cause) will occur; this is almost always in small breeds of dogs.

What are the clinical signs of a dog with tonsillitis?

When the tonsils enlarge, they are usually quite painful. This causes the dog to gag, as if something is in the throat, or to make exaggerated swallowing motions. Some dogs appear to be licking their lips repeatedly. Most affected dogs are reluctant to eat because of the pain associated with swallowing. They may be hungry and go to the food bowl but refuse to eat. Many dogs with tonsillitis are not as active as normal, but they usually do not have fever. This is the one characteristic that differs markedly from people with tonsillitis.

How is tonsillitis treated?

If an underlying source of the infection can be found, it must be treated. Antibiotics are given for 2 - 3 weeks in an effort to rid the tonsils of infection and to treat any other infection that may be present. If the teeth are tartar-laden and infected, they must be cleaned.

What about a tonsillectomy?

That is not the first approach to treatment, but it can become necessary if there is poor response to treatment or if tonsillitis becomes a recurring condition. This is more likely to happen in small breeds of dogs.

Is this contagious to other dogs or to humans?

Most cases of tonsillitis are caused by bacteria that normally are found in the mouth of dogs and humans. Therefore, it is not contagious unless it is caused by an unusual bacterium.

Can Strep throat be associated with dogs?

Streptococcus pyogenes, the cause of "strep throat" in humans does not cause tonsillitis in dogs or cats. However, dogs and cats can acquire a transient infection with this bacterium when they are in contact with a human with strep throat. Although they do not get strep throat, they may harbor the bacterium and serve as a source of it for other human infections. Therefore, it is suggested that dogs be treated when family members have strep throat, especially if recurring infections occur in the household.

VACCINATION FAILURES

One of a veterinarians' greatest frustrations occurs when a dog develops a disease against which it has been vaccinated. There are five possible reasons for this.

- **Ineffective Vaccine**

  Vaccine production is closely regulated by government and manufacturers require a license for each vaccine they produce. Vaccines made by licensed manufacturers are potent at the time they leave the factory; however, several things may happen to inactivate them. The most common cause of vaccine inactivation is that the vaccine has been allowed to become too warm. Temperature is critical to maintaining potency. If vaccine gets too warm during shipment to the distributor or while being stored at the distributor, it is inactivated. This could be a problem associated with vaccines purchased by mail or from non-veterinary suppliers. The buyer has no way to determine whether the vaccines were handled properly during shipment to non-veterinary suppliers. Veterinarians routinely refuse to accept shipments of vaccine if the vaccine is warm at the time of arrival.

- **Inherent Characteristics Of The Vaccine**

  Although most veterinary vaccines have a very high success rate in dogs, none produce immunity in 100% of the dogs being vaccinated.

- **The Dog Is Not Healthy**

  It is mandatory for the patient's immune system to function properly in order to respond to vaccine challenge. If the immune system is very immature, it cannot do so. If the patient has a disease that suppresses the immune system, it will not respond. If the patient has fever, the immune system will be so "occupied" with the fever that it will respond only poorly to vaccine.

- **Breed Differences**

  Certain breeds of dogs have been found to be especially susceptible to certain viruses. This has been observed for years, but recently it has been most obvious in Rottweiler dogs and parvovirus. A disproportionate number of Rottweilers that have been properly vaccinated will develop parvovirus infection.

- **Interference Due To Maternal Antibodies**

  When a puppy is born, it receives immunity-producing proteins from its mother. These are called maternal antibodies. Maternal antibodies protect the newborn from the diseases against which the mother was protected. Maternal antibodies only last a few weeks in the puppy; their duration is directly proportional to the level of immunity the mother has. If her immunity level against rabies, for example, is very high, the maternal antibodies for rabies may last up to 3 months. If her level is low, they may persist only 5 or 6 weeks. As long as they are present, the puppy is protected; however, those antibodies also block a vaccine challenge. If a puppy receives a vaccination for rabies before the rabies antibodies are gone, the vaccine's effect is blocked, and no immunity develops. The same holds true for the other components of the vaccines; temporary immunity received from the mother can interfere with all of the vaccinations. Parvovirus seems to provide maternal immunity which lasts for quite a long time; up to 4 months in some dogs. For this reason, some situations are best handled if a single booster to parvo is given after the puppy series of vaccinations has been completed. This is usually done at about 20 weeks.

  Ideally, a vaccination should be given just after the maternal antibodies are gone but before the puppy is exposed to the disease-causing virus or bacterium. However, it is not practical to determine just when the maternal antibodies are gone for each of the possible diseases. It can be done, but the expense would be tremendous. A vaccination schedule consists of a series of vaccinations given at regular intervals. The timing of this plan is successful in the vast majority of situations. However, if the maternal antibodies are gone and the puppy is exposed to the disease-causing virus or bacterium before the next vaccination occurs, the patient will usually develop the disease.

  The solution to this dilemma would be to give several vaccinations on a pre-determined schedule. If the premise is known to be infected with a particular disease-causing agent, we may recommend vaccinating every 10 to 14 days from age 6 weeks to 20 weeks. The disadvantage for such a plan is the expense. Instead of giving 3 vaccinations in the series, we would be giving 6 or 8, thus the cost would be considerably greater. The potential benefits and risks of extra vaccinations can be discussed with your veterinarian.

VACCINES AND VACCINATION

What is a vaccine?

The word vaccine comes from the Latin word for cow (vacca) and the term was first used in honor of the English country doctor, Edward Jenner. Dr. Jenner discovered that by inoculating the skin of people with a preparation ('vaccine') of material from the common cattle disease, cowpox (or vaccinia), those 'vaccinated' individuals were subsequently protected against the dreaded disease smallpox. Smallpox is caused by a virus closely related to cowpox. The concept of using a mild infection to protect against a severe disease caused by a related organism, was extended by the famous French scientist, Louis Pasteur. Pasteur and his colleagues were able to produce less harmful ('attenuated') forms of organisms such as rabies which could be used as "vaccines" to induce protection or 'immunity'.

What is 'immunity'?

Immunity is a complex series of defenses by which an animal is able to resist an infection or, at the minimum, resist the harmful consequences of the infection. The main components of these defences are the white blood cells; especially lymphocytes and their chemical products: antibodies and cytokines such as interferon. All infectious disease organisms (viruses, bacteria, protozoa, fungi, etc.) have specific components called 'antigens'. These antigens cause lymphocytes to respond in a specific way such that each antigen stimulates the production of a mirror-image 'antibody', as well as non-antibody responses called 'cellular immunity'. Immunity has memory but the memory can fade, sometimes quite rapidly.

Immunity is not absolute. In most cases an animal will still become infected but it can limit the infection, and in the process immunity is 'boosted'. Immunity can sometimes be overcome in cases where there is overwhelming exposure to a high dose of infection, or when the animal is unduly stressed.

What is a live-modified vaccine?

In a live-modified or live-attenuated vaccine the causative organism (virus, bacterium, etc.) has been altered (modified) so that it is no longer harmful ('virulent'), but upon injection or other administration, it will stimulate protective immunity.

What is a killed vaccine?

The organism has been killed ('inactivated') to render it harmless. Killed vaccines often need a helper or 'adjuvant' to stimulate a lasting immune response.

Which is better: live or killed vaccine?

Both have advantages and disadvantages. Your veterinarian takes many circumstances into account in making the choice.

Why a 'needle'?

Some vaccines are given 'locally', for example into the nose, but most require injection so that the maximum take-up of vaccine by the white cells and the immune system is achieved. Some vaccines are injected into subcutaneous (under-the-skin) sites, others into the muscles (intramuscular). Injections look easy but there are a number of precautions a veterinarian is taking.

Which vaccines are needed in dogs?

Depending on your locality some infections may be more or less likely. Your vet will assess the relative risks based on your circumstances, and advise you accordingly. The range of vaccines available includes distemper, hepatitis, parvovirus, leptospirosis, parainfluenza, adenovirus type-2, canine coronavirus, rabies, and *Bordetella bronchiseptica*. These vaccines are often available in combinations. These are convenient and avoid extra 'needles'!

Why is more than one dose of vaccine given to pups?

There are two reasons. First, without complicated testing it is impossible to know when a pup has lost the immunity it gets from its mother (maternal antibody). An early decline in a puppy's maternal antibody can leave it susceptible to infection at a very young age and a strong maternal immunity can actually interfere with early vaccination (*see* Vaccination Failure). Second, particularly with killed vaccines, the first dose is a 'priming' dose, and the second dose boosts the response to a higher, longer-lasting immunity.

Why annual revaccinations?

In most properly-vaccinated dogs, the immunity should last more than a year, and often several years. However immunity does decline with time, and this decline rate varies with individuals. Therefore to maintain the best immunity in a reasonable way, annual revaccinations have proven very successful.

How long does it take for a vaccine to work?

Within a few hours of vaccination the earliest phases of the immune response are being stimulated. However it is usually 10 to 14 days before a reasonable level of protection is established, and with killed vaccines it may not be until after the second dose is given. Also in young puppies maternal antibody may hinder protection until later in the vaccine series. Therefore it is advisable to keep a recently vaccinated pup away from other dogs until it has finished its vaccination course.

What happens if my dog is unwell when vaccinated?

The veterinary check-up prior to vaccination, and sometimes blood tests pre-vaccination, helps prevent this situation. In most cases it would not have disastrous consequences but it is important that an animal is completely healthy when vaccinated, to ensure proper development of immunity.

Will vaccination make my dog sick?

It is not unusual to detect some lethargy in the day or so after vaccination. In the case of killed vaccines with adjuvants, some thickening or lump formation may occur at the vaccination site. If this is obviously painful or persists for more than a week or so with no decrease in size, consult your veterinarian. A few dogs will develop more severe reactions which are forms of hypersensitivity (allergy). These will usually occur within minutes but may be delayed for a few hours. The dog may have difficulty breathing, salivate, vomit, and have diarrhea. In these situations consult your veterinarian immediately.

VOMITING

What causes vomiting?

Vomiting is not a disease; rather, it is a symptom of many different diseases. Many cases of vomiting are self-limiting after a few days. Less commonly, vomiting may result from a serious illness, such as cancer. Even when vomiting is caused by mild illnesses, it may lead to death of the animal if treatment is not begun early enough to prevent severe fluid and nutrient losses.

How serious is vomiting in dogs?

We attempt to determine how sick the dog has become as a consequence of the vomiting. When the dog is systemically ill (i.e., more than one body system is involved), some of the following may be noted:

- Diarrhea
- Dehydration
- Loss of appetite
- Abdominal pain
- High fever
- Lethargy
- Bloody vomiting

What types of tests are performed to find the cause?

If vomiting is associated with several of the above signs, we perform a series of tests in the hope that a diagnosis may be made. When this can be done, more specific treatment may be initiated. Diagnostic tests may include radiography (x-rays) with or without barium, blood tests, biopsies of the stomach and intestinal tract, and exploratory abdominal surgery. Once the diagnosis is known, treatment may include special medications, diets, and/or surgery.

If your dog does not appear systemically ill from the vomiting, the cause may be less serious. Some of the minor causes of vomiting include stomach or intestinal viruses, stomach or intestinal parasites, and dietary indiscretions (such as eating garbage or other offensive or irritating materials). A minimum number of tests are performed to rule out certain parasites and infections. These cases may be treated with drugs to control the motility of the intestinal tract, drugs that relieve inflammation in the intestinal tract, and, often, a special diet for a few days. This approach allows the body's healing mechanisms to correct the problem. Improvement is expected within 2 - 4 days; if this does not occur, we will make a change in medication or perform further tests to better understand the problem. Please keep your veterinarian informed of lack of expected improvement so that the situation may be managed properly.

VON WILLEBRAND'S DISEASE

What is von Willebrand's disease?

von Willebrand's disease (VWD) is the most common inherited bleeding disorder of both man and animals. It is caused by a deficiency in the amount of a protein needed to help platelets (a blood cell used in clotting) seal broken blood vessels. The deficient protein is called "von Willebrand factor antigen".

Which breeds are most commonly affected by VWD?

About 30 different breeds are known to be affected but the Doberman Pinscher is the breed most commonly associated with this disease. Of 15,000 Dobermans screened, more than 70% were found to be carriers of the disease. Fortunately, most of these are not clinically affected (i.e., we see no evidence of bleeding). However, the number of Dobermans with a history of bleeding appears to be on the rise. Although Dobermans are commonly affected, they usually have the mildest form of the disease. Dobermans are, on average, four years-old before diagnosis is made. One study showed that 30% of Scotties and 28% of Shelties had abnormally low concentrations of von Willebrand factor. Chesapeake Bay Retrievers and Scotties are affected with the most severe form of the disease.

What are some of the signs of VWD?

Many dogs with VWD never show outward evidence of having the disease. Others may hemorrhage from the nose, vagina, urinary bladder or oral mucous membranes; prolonged bleeding after trauma or surgery is common. Females may bleed excessively after giving birth. In affected dogs with uncontrolled hemorrhage, death may occur.

How is VWD diagnosed?

A screening test, called the buccal mucosal screening time, may be performed in the veterinarian's office. Prolonged bleeding on this test can raise the suspicion of the disease, especially in breeds known to be at risk. For owners who wish to confirm the diagnosis, it is possible to determine the exact amount of von Willebrand protein present in the blood. Owners of Dobermans often report that the pet has undergone routine ovariohysterectomy (spay) or castration, ear trim, and tail docking as a pup. An uncomplicated recovery from such procedures does not eliminate the possibility that a dog may be affected; some dogs do not become obvious "bleeders" until later in life.

Are there any situations which pose an increased risk if my dog is affected?

The avoidance of certain medications is critical for the dog with VWD. Drugs that may precipitate a bleeding crisis in the dog include the following:

- Ampicillin/Amoxicillin
- Aspirin
- Antihistamines
- Estrogens
- Heparin
- Ibuprofen
- Penicillin
- Phenothiazine tranquilizers
- Phenylbutazone
- Sulfa-based antibiotics
- Theophylline

These drugs should be avoided when possible, but especially when the dog is in a bleeding crisis.

Emotional stress is thought to precipitate bleeding in humans with the disease. The subjective nature of such a finding makes it difficult to know if is a similar association in dogs but it remains a possibility.

What can be done to treat dogs with VWD?

In an emergency situation, transfusion of blood or fresh frozen plasma may stabilize the patient. The dog donating blood may be treated with a drug called DDAVP prior to blood collection which will raise the level of von Willebrand factor in the donor's blood, an obvious benefit to the recipient.

Some dogs with VWD are able to increase the amount of protein in circulation after the administration of DDAVP, although the response is variable. At this time, it is not recommended to use this drug on a regular basis. The drug is expensive, and not all dogs will respond to it.

If I own a Doberman that has always been healthy, should I do something?

Since many affected Dobermans will never have bleeding problems, any recommendation to do routine testing is debatable. However, identification of dogs that have abnormal bleeding times can be very valuable if surgery is planned. Additionally, knowing that your dog is a carrier of VWD can be very important if an injury occurs.

WHIPWORMS

What are whipworms?

Whipworms are intestinal parasites which are about 1/4 inch (6 mm) long. They live in the large intestine (cecum and colon) of dogs where they cause severe irritation to the lining of these organs. This results in watery, bloody diarrhea, weight loss, and general debilitation. They are one of the most pathogenic (harmful) worms found in dogs.

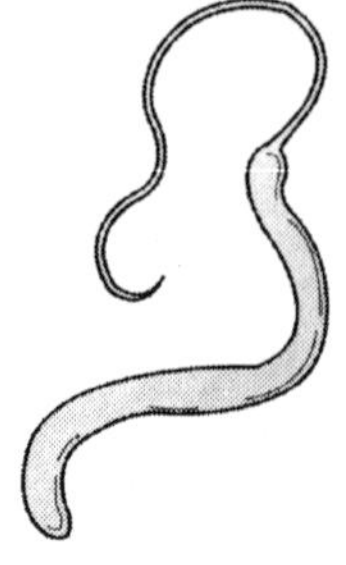

Whipworm (2x actual size)

How did my dog get whipworms?

Whipworms pass microscopic eggs in the stool. The eggs are very resistant to drying and heat, so they can remain viable in the dog's environment for years. They mature and are able to reinfect the dog in 10 - 60 days. The eggs are swallowed and return to the lower intestinal tract to complete the life cycle.

How is whipworm infection diagnosed?

Whipworms are diagnosed by finding eggs with a microscopic examination of the stool. However, multiple samples are often required because these parasites pass small numbers of eggs on an irregular basis. Any dog with chronic diarrhea can be reasonably suspected to have whipworms, regardless of several negative stool examinations. It is an accepted practice to treat for whipworms based on assumption of infection. Response to treatment is an indication that whipworms were present but could not be detected on fecal examination.

How are whipworms treated?

There are several drugs that are very effective against whipworms. Two treatments are needed at a 3 - 4 week interval, but because reinfection is such a problem, it is advisable to treat again every 3 - 4 months or to put the dog on a heartworm preventive which also prevents whipworms. Whipworms are not nearly as common now because of widespread use of the heartworm preventives which help to control whipworms.

Please note that although several heartworm preventative products block infection by several kinds of intestinal worms, some do not prevent infection with whipworms.

Can I get whipworms from my dog?

Whipworms are not infectious to people; they are only parasites of the dog.

What is the Wobbler Syndrome?

The term "wobbler" originated from a spinal disease of horses that causes lack of coordination while walking. The canine version is more appropriately known as Caudal Cervical Spondylomyelopathy. It results in a wobbly gait when walking or running due to pressure on the spinal cord in the lower part of the neck. Many of these dogs stumble when walking, and the rear legs may be affected first.

How does it happen?

This disease begins because there is an instability between two or more vertebrae in the lower part of the neck. When instability exists, the body attempts to correct the problem. This results in a thickening of the ligaments that are within the joint; one is above the spinal cord and two are below it. As these ligaments thicken, they put pressure on the spinal cord.

The spinal cord is much like a large telephone cable that contains thousands of wires, each carrying important messages. When the telephone cable is crushed, the tiny wires within are broken so they cannot transmit information. A similar event occurs when the spinal cord is compressed by the thickened ligaments. They are unable to carry messages from the brain to the nerves in the legs, so the legs cannot move as they should.

My dog is paralyzed in all four legs. Is this part of this disease?

Yes. The pressure on the spinal cord from the thickened ligaments causes the dog to walk in a very uncoordinated fashion. However, another event often follows. The instability present between the vertebrae also puts unnatural stress on the disk that is located between the bones. After weeks or months of stress, the disk will rupture. When this happens, the pressure on the spinal cord is so great that paralysis occurs. This may involve only the front legs or, in other cases, all four legs.

Are certain breeds of dogs more commonly affected than others?

Yes. Great Danes and Doberman Pinchers are the commonly affected breeds, but any large breed is at risk for this disorder. Great Danes are usually affected when they are young, about 1 - 3 years of age. Doberman Pinchers and other breeds are typically 6 - 9 years of age when the symptoms begin.

How is the diagnosis made?

Radiographs (x-rays) of the neck often reveal that the cervical vertebrae are not properly aligned. If the dog is the right breed and the symptoms are correct, this provides strong evidence of the wobbler syndrome. However, plain radiographs do not show the spinal cord so the presence of pressure on it cannot be proven in this manner. A myelogram is a radiograph made after a special contrast material (dye) is injected around the spinal cord. The dye outlines the cord so that points of pressure can be readily observed. A myelogram is needed to give conclusive evidence of the wobbler syndrome. It requires general anesthesia.

What is the treatment?

Anti-inflammatory drugs and pain relievers are often prescribed in the early stages of this disease. They may provide some relief from the symptoms, but this improvement is only temporary. As the disease progresses, medication will no longer be helpful. Special precautions must be taken when pain relievers and anti-inflammatory medications are given to Doberman Pinschers as there is a high incidence of inherited bleeding disorders in this breed; some medications may precipitate a bleeding crisis.

In some dogs, a specially-fashioned neck brace can be helpful in limiting motion in the neck. This can be helpful in some dogs, especially dogs for which surgery is not feasible. However, most dogs have progressive disease and are helped best with prompt surgery.

Successful treatment requires that the pressure be removed from the spinal cord. There are several surgical procedures that have been used, but none have been successful in all cases. The findings on the myelogram are used to determine the surgical procedure that is most likely to be helpful.

What is involved with after care?

The degree of after care will depend on the dog's ability to walk at the time it goes home from the hospital. If it can walk, but it is uncoordinated, it will need assistance so that a fall does not occur. If it is still paralyzed at the time of discharge, the amount of after care can be considerable because of the dog's weight. If you are not able to lift your dog and you do not have someone else who can help you do so, you should discuss this situation before you opt for surgery.

What is the prognosis?

If surgery is performed at the time the dog is uncoordinated, there is a fairly good chance of success. If paralysis of all four legs has occurred, the success rate is less.

Index

024A